AA

THE DRIVING TEST

PASS
FIRST TIME

PRACTICAL

By
Linda Hatswell B Ed (Hons)

 The Driving School

Published by AA Publishing (a trading name of
Automobile Association Developments Limited,
whose registered office is Norfolk House,
Priestley Road, Basingstoke,
Hampshire RG24 9NY.
Registered Number 1878835.)

A catalogue record for this book is available
from the British Library

ISBN 0 7495 1409 4

Edited by Susan Gordon

Printed in Spain

THE DRIVING TEST
PASS
FIRST TIME
PRACTICAL

Foreword

You want to pass the driving test and take advantage of the freedom and mobility that driving a car can give you. Do the following three things and you will achieve your objective — passing the test:

1

Learn and understand the **skills** of driving by taking lessons from a trained and fully qualified driving instructor.

2

Acquire the **knowledge** of the rules through your instructor and by studying *The Highway Code*. A key element of learning is to test and reinforce your knowledge. This book is specially designed for this purpose.

3

Take the right **attitude**. No one is a 'natural' or a 'perfect driver'. All drivers make mistakes. Be careful, courteous and considerate to all other road users.

Using this book shows you have the right attitude to learning to drive. So, remember, acquire the **skills**, the **knowledge** and the right **attitude** and you will pass the test!

Nick Bravery, Business manager

 The Driving School

6 Contents

Part 9

Part 10

Part 11

Part 12

Part 13

Part 14

Part 15

Part 16

Part 17

About this book

This book is aimed at those who are learning or are about to learn how to drive.

No book can teach you how to drive. This is best left to an Approved Driving Instructor who has proven skill and ability. This book will, however, help you test your knowledge of the theoretical aspects of driving.

A thorough knowledge of driving theory is becoming increasingly important, especially in view of the harmonisation of driving tests throughout the European Community states, due to take place by 1996. Most EC countries have a knowledge or theory test as well as a practical test of driving ability.

This book is designed to be easy to follow and is made up of questions, many of which use diagrams and illustrations, that test your knowledge of driving on today's roads. We have included a section on the driving test itself: what do you really know about taking the test and what is expected of you? And of course learning to drive does not stop with passing the test. It continues throughout life, and the new experiences and challenges it will bring such as driving on the Continent and dealing with a road accident are also covered here.

How to use this book

It is strongly recommended that you learn to drive with an Approved Driving Instructor. All AA The Driving School's franchised instructors are fully qualified and have passed the AA's own strict test of instructional ability. The Driving School offers a programme of planned tuition which includes frequent checks to keep you up to date with your own progress, ensuring that you are fully prepared and ready to pass your test.

The book is divided into clearly defined sections. Each deals with a particular requirement of the test, for example reverse parallel parking, aspects of car control or road procedure. A recognised syllabus is followed, each heading being indentifiable as a subject that needs to be covered when learning to drive. The questions are colour coded, matching the answers which are to be found towards the back of the book.

The best method of working is to read the question, write in your answer, then check what you have written against the answer we have given. If you need further explanation, we suggest you refer to the HMSO publications *Driving, Your Driving Test* and *The Highway Code*, all of which are available from AA shops.

The book is written so that it can be used either in conjunction with taking driving lessons, at home to test your knowledge of the subjects covered on your lessons, or between lessons to review the work covered.

With the increase in traffic and today's complex systems, it is not enough to be able to drive a car. You need to know that you fully understand all road procedures, traffic signs — and much more. This book will test how much knowledge you really have and will help you to be a safer driver on the road.

Good defensive driving depends on adopting the right attitude from the start. These questions will test your knowledge of what is required before you even sit in the driver's seat.

 What do you need before you can drive on a public road?

Answer _____

 The best way to learn is to have regular planned tuition with an ADI (Approved Driving Instructor).

An ADI is someone who has taken and passed all three driving instructor's

e_ _ _ _ _ _ _ _ _ _ _ _ _ and is on the official r_ _ _ _ _ _ _ _

Complete the sentence

 Anyone supervising a learner must be at least _ _ years old and must have held (and still hold) a full licence (motor car) for at least

t_ _ _ _ _ years.   Complete the sentence

Q4 Your tuition vehicle must display L-plates.

Where should they be placed?

Answer _____

ANSWERS ON PAGE 112

Young and inexperienced drivers are more vulnerable.

Is this true or false?   Answer _____

 Showing responsibility to yourself and others is the key to being

a safe driver.

Ask yourself, would you . . .

YES   NO

1 Want to drive with someone who has been drinking?

2 Want to drive with someone who takes risks and puts other lives at risk?

3 Want to drive with someone who does not concentrate?

4 Want to drive with someone who drives too fast?

 Do you want to be a safe and responsible driver?

YES   NO

Tick the appropriate box

ANSWERS ON PAGE 112

To use the controls safely you need to adopt a suitable driving position. There are a number of checks you should make.

Fill in the missing words

1 Check the h_ _ _ _ _ _ _ _ _ _ is on.

2 Check the d_ _ _ _ _ are shut.

3 Check your s_ _ _ _ is in the correct position.

4 Check the h_ _ _ _ r_ _ _ _ _ _ _ _ _ is adjusted to give maximum protection.

5 Check the driving m_ _ _ _ _ _ _ are adjusted to give maximum rear view.

6 Check your s_ _ _ _ b_ _ _ _ is securely fastened.

ANSWERS ON PAGE 112

Here is a list of controls and a list of functions.

Match each control to its function by placing the appropriate letter in the box

The controls   The functions

☐ The handbrake   A   To control the direction in which you want to travel

☐ The driving mirrors   B   To slow or stop the vehicle

☐ The gear lever   C   To increase or decrease the engine's speed

☐ The clutch   D   To give you a clear view behind

☐ The steering wheel   E   To hold the vehicle still when it is stationary

☐ The foot-brake   F   To enable you to change gear

☐ The accelerator   G   To enable you to make or break contact between the engine and the wheels

Fill in the missing word   The accelerator can also be called the g_ _ _ pedal.

Q10   Which foot should you use for each of these controls (in cars with a manual gearbox)?   R = Right foot   L = Left foot

☐ The foot-brake   ☐ The clutch   ☐ The accelerator

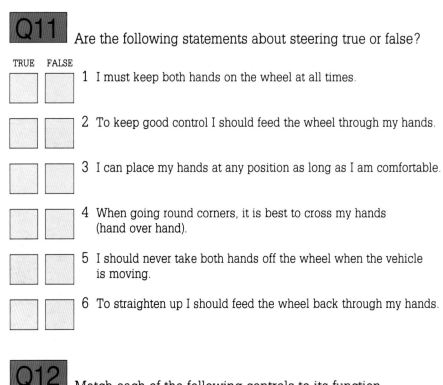

Q11 Are the following statements about steering true or false?

TRUE FALSE

1 I must keep both hands on the wheel at all times.

2 To keep good control I should feed the wheel through my hands.

3 I can place my hands at any position as long as I am comfortable.

4 When going round corners, it is best to cross my hands (hand over hand).

5 I should never take both hands off the wheel when the vehicle is moving.

6 To straighten up I should feed the wheel back through my hands.

Q12 Match each of the following controls to its function.

The controls

The direction indicators

Dipped beam

Main beam

Rear fog lamp

Horn

Hazard lights

The functions

A To enable you to see the road ahead and other road users to see you without causing dazzle

B To show other road users which way you intend to turn

C To use only when visibility is 100m/yds or less

D To enable you to see further, but not to be used when there is oncoming traffic

E To warn other road users of your presence

F To warn other road users when you are temporarily obstructing traffic

Q1 The following is a list of actions involved in moving off from rest.

Number the boxes 1 to 9 to show the correct sequence

The first box has been filled in to give you a start

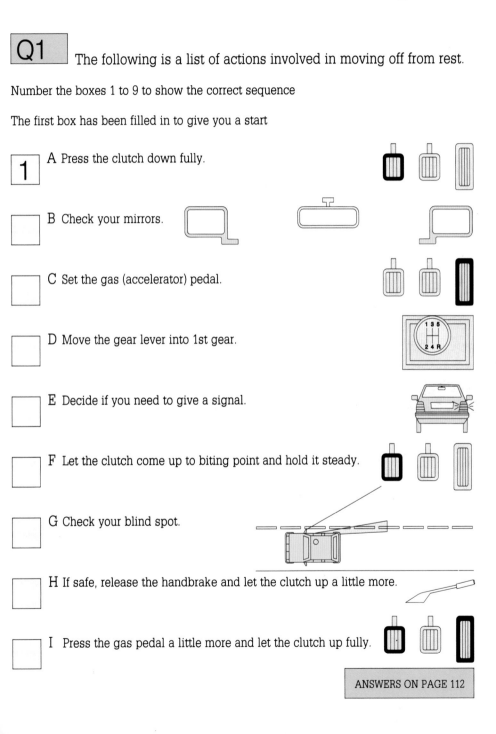

1 A Press the clutch down fully.

B Check your mirrors.

C Set the gas (accelerator) pedal.

D Move the gear lever into 1st gear.

E Decide if you need to give a signal.

F Let the clutch come up to biting point and hold it steady.

G Check your blind spot.

H If safe, release the handbrake and let the clutch up a little more.

I Press the gas pedal a little more and let the clutch up fully.

ANSWERS ON PAGE 112

Q2 The following is a list of actions required for stopping normally.

Number the boxes 1 to 9 to show the correct sequence. The first box has been filled

in to give you a start

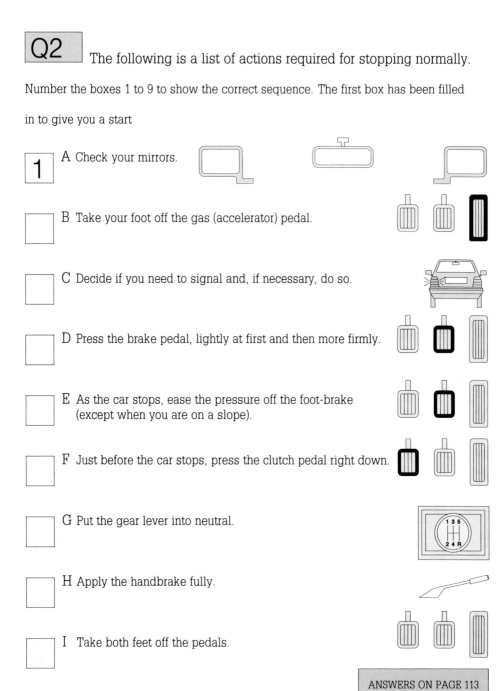

1 A Check your mirrors.

B Take your foot off the gas (accelerator) pedal.

C Decide if you need to signal and, if necessary, do so.

D Press the brake pedal, lightly at first and then more firmly.

E As the car stops, ease the pressure off the foot-brake (except when you are on a slope).

F Just before the car stops, press the clutch pedal right down.

G Put the gear lever into neutral.

H Apply the handbrake fully.

I Take both feet off the pedals.

ANSWERS ON PAGE 113

Gears enable you to select the power you need from the engine to perform a particular task.

 Which gear gives you the most power?

Answer ☐

 If you were travelling at 60 mph on a clear road, which gear would you most likely select?

Answer ☐

 When approaching and turning a corner, as shown in the diagram, which gear would you most likely use?

Answer ☐

 You need to change gear to match your e _ _ _ _ _ _ speed to the speed at which your v _ _ _ _ _ _ _ is travelling. The s _ _ _ _ _ the engine is making will help you know w _ _ _ _ to change gear.

Complete the sentences

ANSWERS ON PAGE 113

Number the boxes to show the correct sequence of actions required when changing up.

The first box has been filled in for you

| 1 | A Place your left hand on the gear lever. |

B Move the gear lever to the next highest position.

C Press the clutch pedal down fully and ease off the gas pedal.

D Let the clutch pedal come up fully and, at the same time, press the gas pedal.

E Put your left hand back on the steering wheel.

ANSWERS ON PAGE 113

Are the following statements about changing down true or false?

Tick the appropriate boxes

TRUE   FALSE

1 I would stay in the highest gear as long as possible, even if my engine started to labour.

2 I would change down early so that the engine helps to slow the car down.

3 I would avoid using the foot-brake as much as possible.

4 I would usually slow the car down by using the foot-brake first. Then, when I am at the required speed, I would change down to the appropriate gear.

5 I would always change down through the gears so that I do not miss out any intermediate gears.

ANSWERS ON PAGE 113

Q9 When changing gear, I should look . . .

1 Ahead   2 At the gear lever   3 At my feet

☐ Which is correct?

ANSWERS ON PAGE 113

Q10 Do's and don'ts

DO   DON'T

☐ ☐   1 Force the gear lever if there is any resistance

☐ ☐   2 Rush the gear changes

☐ ☐   3 Match your speed with the correct gear

☐ ☐   4 Use the brakes, where necessary, to reduce speed before changing down

☐ ☐   5 Listen to the sound of the engine

☐ ☐   6 Take your eyes off the road when changing gear

☐ ☐   7 Hold the gear lever longer than necessary

☐ ☐   8 Coast with the clutch down or the gear lever in neutral

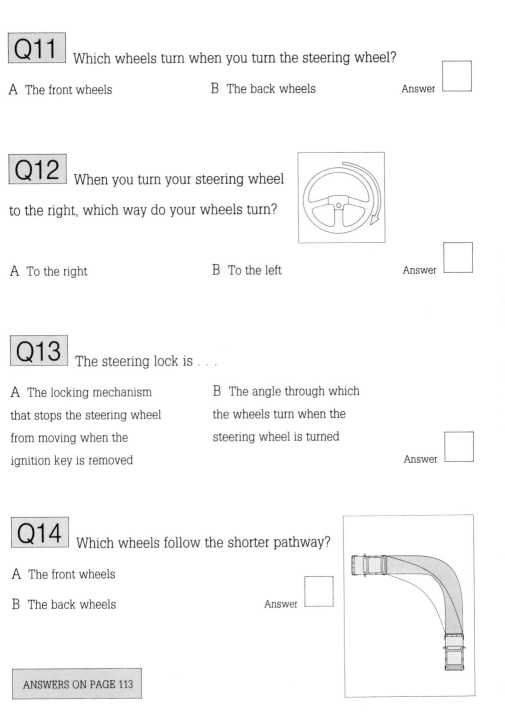

Q11 Which wheels turn when you turn the steering wheel?

A The front wheels   B The back wheels   Answer

Q12 When you turn your steering wheel
to the right, which way do your wheels turn?

A To the right   B To the left   Answer

Q13 The steering lock is . . .

A The locking mechanism   B The angle through which
that stops the steering wheel   the wheels turn when the
from moving when the   steering wheel is turned
ignition key is removed   Answer

Q14 Which wheels follow the shorter pathway?

A The front wheels

B The back wheels   Answer

ANSWERS ON PAGE 113

Which is the correct position for normal driving?

Put letter A, B or C in the box

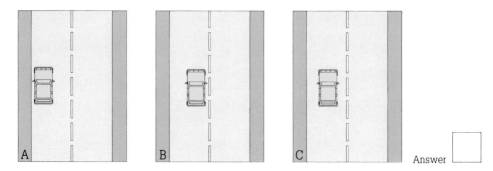

A   B   C   Answer

 Q16 Which diagram shows the correct pathway when driving normally?

Put a letter A or B in the box

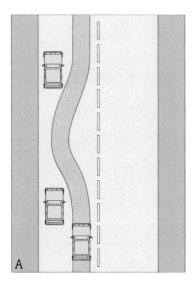

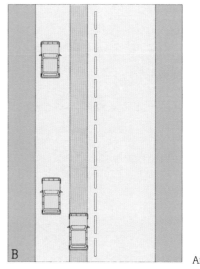

A   B   Answer

ANSWERS ON PAGE 113

Pushing the clutch pedal down . . .

A Releases the engine from the wheels

B Engages the engine with the wheels   Answer ☐

 The point where the clutch plates meet is called the

b _ _ _ _ _ point.

Fill in the missing word

 By controlling the amount of contact between the clutch plates,

it is possible to control the speed of the car. Would you use this control . . .

YES   NO

☐   ☐   1 When moving away from rest?

☐   ☐   2 When manoeuvring the car in reverse gear?

☐   ☐   3 When slowing down to turn a corner?

☐   ☐   4 In very slow moving traffic?

☐   ☐   5 To slow the car down?

ANSWERS ON PAGE 114

A junction is a point where t_ _ _ o_ m_ _ _ _ r_ _ _ _ _ meet.

Complete the sentence

 Here are five main types of junction. Name them

 Match these road signs to the junctions shown above.

Put letters A, B, C, D and E in the boxes

1   2   3   4   5

 What do these signs mean?

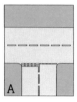

1 Stop and give way

2 Slow down, look, and proceed if safe

3 Give way to traffic on the major road

A

Answer   Put a number in each box   Answer

At every junction you should follow a safe routine.

Put the following into the correct order by numbering the boxes 1 to 5

☐ Signal   ☐ Speed   ☐ Position   ☐ Mirrors   ☐ Look

 The diagram shows a car turning right into a minor road. The boxes are numbered to show the correct sequence of actions.

Complete the sentence

At point 5 you should look and a _ _ _ _ _ _ the situation, d _ _ _ _ _ _ to go or wait, and a _ _ accordingly.

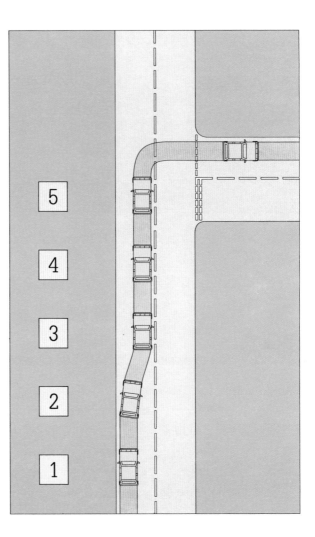

ANSWERS ON PAGE 114

Turning left into a minor road

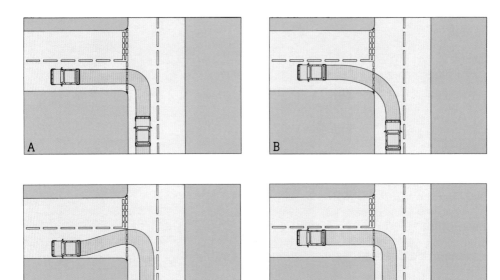

Which diagram shows the best path to follow when driving a motor car A, B, C or D?

Answer

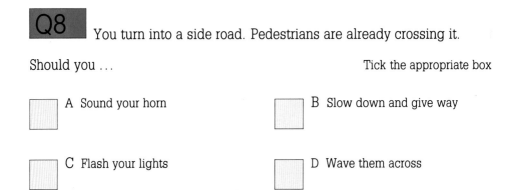

You turn into a side road. Pedestrians are already crossing it.

Should you ...   Tick the appropriate box

A Sound your horn   B Slow down and give way

C Flash your lights   D Wave them across

Q9   Turning right into a minor road

ANSWERS ON PAGE 114

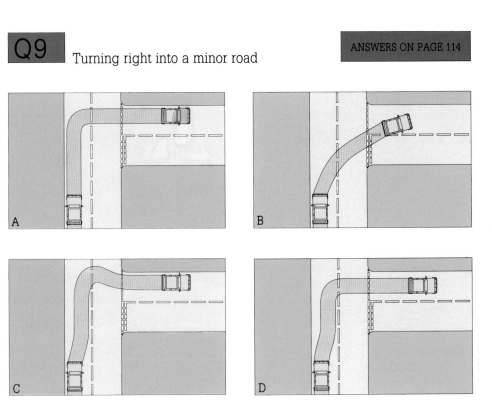

Which diagram shows the best path to follow A, B, C or D?

Answer

Q10   These are the golden rules for emerging from junctions.

Complete the sentences

1 Always use your m _ _ _ _ _ _ _ to check the speed and

   p _ _ _ _ _ _ _ _ of vehicles behind.

2 Always cancel your s _ _ _ _ _ _.

3 Speed up to a s _ _ _ speed after joining the new road.

4 Keep a s _ _ _ _ d _ _ _ _ _ _ _ _ _ between you and the vehicle ahead.

5 Do not attempt to o _ _ _ _ _ _ _ _ until you can assess the new road.

All crossroads must be approached with caution.

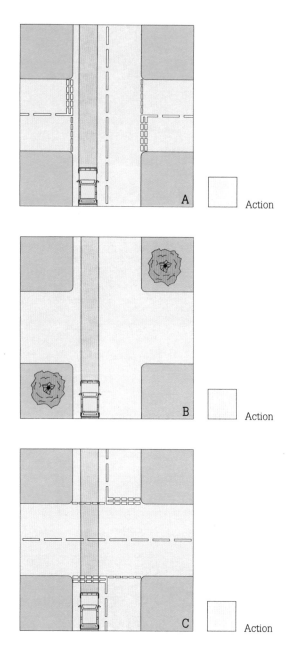

A ☐ Action

B ☐ Action

C ☐ Action

Match Actions 1, 2 and 3 listed below with these diagrams

Actions

1 Approach with caution, look well ahead and be prepared to stop. Remember other drivers may assume they have priority.

2 Look well ahead, slow down and be prepared to give way to traffic on the major road.

3 Look well ahead and into the side roads for approaching vehicles. Remember other drivers may not give you priority.

ANSWERS ON PAGE 114

Q12 Which of the following statements describes the correct

procedure when approaching a roundabout?   Put letter A, B or C in the box

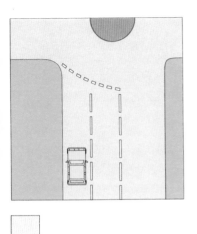

Answer

A The broken white line at a roundabout means I must stop and give way to traffic already on the roundabout.

B The broken white line at a roundabout means I must give priority to traffic already on the roundabout.

C The broken white line means I should give way to any traffic approaching from my immediate right.

Q13 The following sentences give guidance on lane discipline on a

roundabout.   Fill in the missing words

1 When turning left at a roundabout, I should stay in the _ _ _ _ _ -hand lane and should stay in that lane throughout.

2 When going ahead at a roundabout, I should be in the _ _ _ _ _ -hand lane, and should stay in that lane throughout unless conditions dictate otherwise.

3 When turning right at a roundabout, I should approach in the

_ _ _ _ _ _ -hand lane, or approach as if turning

right at a junction, and stay in that lane throughout.

ANSWERS ON PAGE 114

The letters A, B and C in the diagram mark places where you should signal.

Complete the sentences

1 I would signal at A when turning _ _ _ _ _ .

2 I would signal at B when g _ _ _ _ _ _ _ _ _ _ _ .

3 I would signal at A and at **C** when turning _ _ _ _ _ _ .

 At a roundabout you should always use a safe routine.

Fill in the missing words

m_ _ _ _ _ _ _ _ , s _ _ _ _ _ _ , p_ _ _ _ _ _ _ _ , s_ _ _ _ _ , l_ _ _ _ .

 What does this sign mean?

1 Roundabout

2 Mini-roundabout

3 Vehicles may pass either side

 Answer

ANSWERS ON PAGES 114-15

Q1 It is safest to park off the road or in a car park whenever possible. If you have to park on the road, think . . . Fill in the missing words

1 Is it s_ _ _ _ ? 2 Is it c_ _ _ _ _ _ _ _ _ _ _ ? 3 Is it l_ _ _ _ _ ?

Q2 In this diagram four of the cars are parked illegally or without consideration of others.

Put the numbers of these cars in the boxes

ANSWERS ON PAGE 115

For reverse parallel parking manoeuvres, see pages 52-3.

The diagram shows
a stationary vehicle on the
left-hand side of the road.

Which has priority,

vehicle 1 or vehicle 2?

 Answer

Obstruction

ANSWER ON PAGE 115

This diagram shows a steep downward hill with an obstruction on the right-hand side of the road.

Which vehicle should be given priority, vehicle 1 or vehicle 2?

 Answer

ANSWER ON PAGE 115

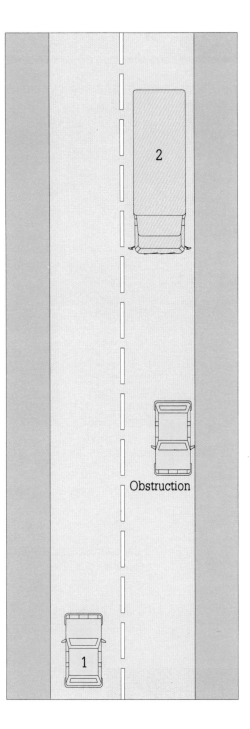

The diagram shows two vehicles, travelling in opposite directions, turning right at a crossroads.

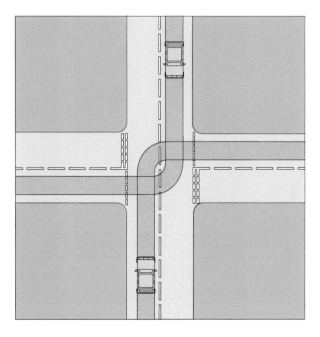

Are these statements true or false? Tick the appropriate boxes

TRUE   FALSE

 1 The safest route is to pass each other offside to offside.

 2 If the approaching vehicle flashes its headlamps, I should turn as quickly as possible.

 3 I should always try to get eye-to-eye contact with the driver of the other vehicle to determine which course to take.

ANSWERS ON PAGE 115

Which of the following factors, illustrated in the diagram, should be taken into consideration when turning right into a side road?

Tick the appropriate boxes

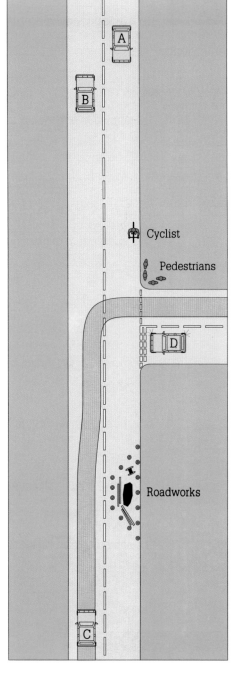

YES NO

1 The speed of the approaching vehicle (A)

2 The roadworks

3 The speed of vehicle B

4 The cyclist

5 Your speed (vehicle C)

6 The pedestrians

7 The car waiting to turn right (D)

ANSWERS ON PAGE 115

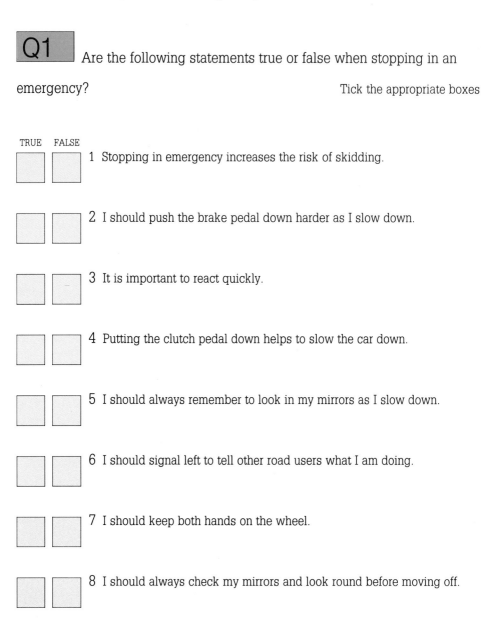

Q1 Are the following statements true or false when stopping in an emergency? Tick the appropriate boxes

TRUE FALSE

☐ ☐ 1 Stopping in emergency increases the risk of skidding.

☐ ☐ 2 I should push the brake pedal down harder as I slow down.

☐ ☐ 3 It is important to react quickly.

☐ ☐ 4 Putting the clutch pedal down helps to slow the car down.

☐ ☐ 5 I should always remember to look in my mirrors as I slow down.

☐ ☐ 6 I should signal left to tell other road users what I am doing.

☐ ☐ 7 I should keep both hands on the wheel.

☐ ☐ 8 I should always check my mirrors and look round before moving off.

ANSWERS ON PAGE 115

Q2 Cadence braking is a technique which can be used in very
slippery conditions in an emergency. *Fill in the missing words*
The technique requires you to p _ _ _ _ the brake pedal. The procedure to
follow is:

1 Apply m _ _ _ _ _ _ _ _ pressure.
2 Release the brake pedal just as the wheels are about to l _ _ _ _ .
3 Then q _ _ _ _ _ _ _ apply the brakes again. Apply and release the
brakes until vehicle has stopped. This technique should only be used in
emergency situations.

Q3 Anti-lock braking systems (ABS)* work in a similar way to
cadence braking. *Fill in the missing words*
When braking in an emergency, ABS brakes allow you to s _ _ _ _ _ and
b _ _ _ _ _ at the same time. You do not have to p _ _ _ the brakes as
you would in cadence braking. When using ABS you keep the
p _ _ _ _ _ _ _ _ applied.
Are these statements about ABS braking true or false? *Tick the correct boxes*

TRUE　FALSE

☐　☐　　1 Cars fitted with ABS braking cannot skid.

ANSWERS ON PAGE 115

☐　☐　　2 I do not need to leave as much room between me and the car in front if
　　　　　I have ABS brakes because I know I can stop in a shorter distance.

* *ABS is a registered trade mark of Bosch (Germany). ABS stands for Anti-Blockiersystem*

The distance taken for a car to reach stopping point divides into thinking distance and braking distance.

 Could these factors affect thinking distance?

Tick the appropriate boxes

YES   NO

 1 The condition of your tyres

2 Feeling tired or unwell

 3 Speed of reaction

 4 Going downhill

 Most drivers' reaction time is well over . . .

Tick the appropriate box

½ second   1 second   5 seconds

 ANSWERS ON PAGE 116

Q6   Stopping distance depends partly on the speed at which the car
is travelling.   Complete the sentences

1 At 30 mph your overall stopping distance will be _ _ metres or _ _ feet.

2 At 50 mph your thinking distance will be _ _ _ metres or _ _ feet.

3 At 70 mph your overall stopping distance will be _ _ metres or _ _ feet.

Q7   Stopping distance also varies according to road conditions.

Complete the sentences

In wet weather your vehicle will take l_ _ _ _ _ to stop. You should

therefore allow m_ _ _ time.

Q8   Too many accidents are caused by drivers driving too close to the

vehicle in front. A safe gap between you and the vehicle in front can be

measured by noting a stationary object and counting in seconds the time

that lapses between the vehicle in front passing that object and your own

vehicle passing that object.   Complete the sentence

Only a fool b_ _ _ _ _ _ the t_ _ _ s_ _ _ _ _ _ rule.

ANSWERS ON PAGE 116

Are these statements about moving off at an angle true or false?

Tick the appropriate boxes

TRUE   FALSE

 1 I should check my mirrors as I am pulling out.

 2 I should check my mirrors and blindspot before I pull out.

 3 I should move out as quickly as possible.

 4 The amount of steering required will depend on how close I am to the vehicle in front.

 5 I should look out for oncoming traffic.

 6 As long as I am signalling, people will know what I am doing. I will be able to pull out because somebody will let me in.

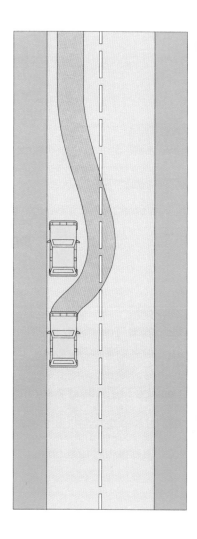

ANSWERS ON PAGE 116

Are these statements about moving off uphill true or false?

Tick the appropriate boxes

TRUE   FALSE

   1   On an uphill gradient the car will tend to roll back.

   2   To stop the car rolling back I need to use more gas.

  3   I do not need to use the handbrake.

   4   The biting point may be slightly higher.

   5   I need to press the gas pedal further than when moving off on the level.

   6   I need to allow more time to pull away.

   7   The main controls I use will be the clutch pedal, the gas pedal and the handbrake.

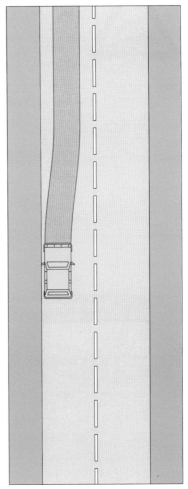

ANSWERS ON PAGE 116

Are these statements about moving off downhill true or false?

Tick the appropriate boxes

TRUE   FALSE

 1 The car will tend to roll forwards.

 2 The main controls I use will be the handbrake, the clutch pedal and the gas pedal.

 3 The only gear I can move off in is 1st gear.

 4 I should release the handbrake while keeping the foot-brake applied.

 5 I should look round just before moving off.

 6 I must not have my foot on the foot-brake as I start to release the clutch.

ANSWERS ON PAGE 116

Q4   The following statements are about approaching a junction when going uphill or downhill. With which do you agree?   Tick the relevant boxes

When going downhill . . .

1 It is more difficult to slow down

2 Putting the clutch down will help slow the car down

3 The higher the gear, the greater the control

4 When changing gear you may need to use the foot-brake at the same time as the clutch

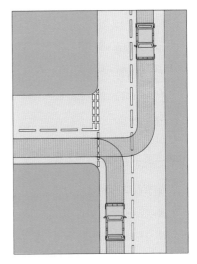

When going uphill . . .

5 Early use of mirrors, signals, brakes, gears and steering will help to position the car correctly

6 You may need to use your handbrake more often

7 When you change gear, the car tends to slow down

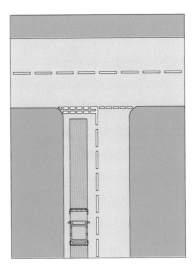

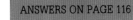
ANSWERS ON PAGE 116

Before reversing there are three things to consider.

Fill in the missing words

1 Is it s_ _ _ _ ?

2 Is it c_ _ _ _ _ _ _ _ _ ?

ANSWERS ON PAGES 116-17

3 Is it within the l_ _ ?

 Are the following statements about reversing true or false?

Tick the appropriate boxes

TRUE   FALSE

1 Other road users should see what I am doing and wait for me.

2 I should wave pedestrians on, so that I can get on with the manoeuvre more quickly.

3 I should avoid being too hesitant.

4 I should avoid making other road users slow down or change course.

 How should you hold the steering wheel when reversing left?

A   B   C   Which is correct?

These statements are all about reversing.

Tick those which you think are correct

☐ 1 My car will respond differently in reverse gear.

☐ 2 My car will feel no different.

☐ 3 Steering is not affected. The car responds the same as when going forward.

☐ 4 The steering will feel different. I will have to wait for the steering to take effect.

 Which way will the rear of the car go when it is reversed?

 Car A

Answer _____

Car B

Answer _____

 It is important to move the vehicle slowly when reversing.

Complete the sentence

Moving the vehicle slowly is safer because

I have control and it allows me to carry

out good o_ _ _ _ _ _ _ _ _ _ _ _ checks.

ANSWERS ON PAGE 117

When reversing good observation is vital. Where should you look?

Tick the correct answer

☐ 1 At the kerb   ☐ 3 Where your car is going

☐ 2 Ahead   ☐ 4 Out of the back window

 Are these statements about reversing round a corner true or false?

Tick the appropriate boxes

TRUE   FALSE

☐ ☐   1 If the corner is sharp, I need to be further away from the kerb.

☐ ☐   2 The distance from the kerb makes no difference.

☐ ☐   3 I should try to stay reasonably close to the kerb all the way round.

 Before reversing I should check . . .   Tick the correct box

☐ 1 Behind me   ☐ 3 My door mirrors

☐ 2 Ahead and to the rear   ☐ 4 All round

ANSWERS ON PAGE 117

This diagram shows a car about to reverse round the corner to the left.

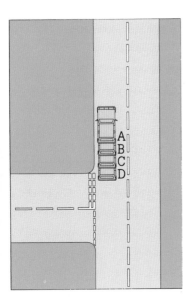

Q10 Which position is the correct one in which to start steering?

A, B, C or D?   Answer

Q11 Which way should you steer?

Answer

Q12 What will happen to the front of the car?   Answer

Q13 Are these statements about steering when reversing round a corner true or false?   Tick the appropriate boxes

TRUE   FALSE

1 The more gradual the corner, the less I have to steer.

2 I need to steer the same for every corner.   ANSWERS ON PAGE 117

3 The sharper the corner, the more I have to steer.

Q14 As I enter the new road I should continue to keep a look-out for

p_ _ _ _ _ _ _ _ _ _ _ and other r_ _ _ _ u_ _ _ _ _ . I should

s_ _ _ _ if necessary.   Complete the sentences

Q15 True or false? When reversing from a major road into a side road on the right, I have to move to the wrong side of the road.

TRUE FALSE

☐ ☐ Tick the appropriate box

Q16 Which diagram shows the correct path to follow when moving to the right-hand side of the road?

A or B?

☐ Answer

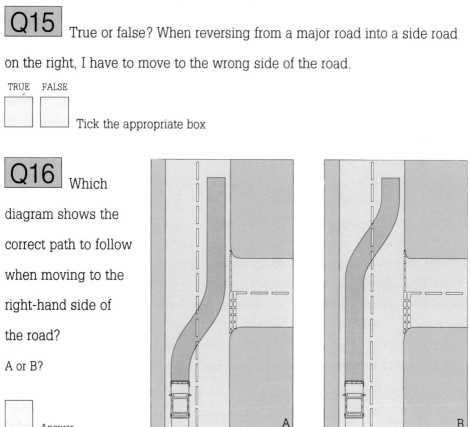

A

B

Q17 Which of the following correctly describes your sitting position for reversing to the right?

1 I will need to sit so that I can see over my right shoulder.

2 I will need to sit so that I can see over my right shoulder, ahead and to the left.

3 My position is the same as when reversing to the left.

☐ Answer

ANSWERS ON PAGE 117

Q18 True or false? I may need to change my hand
position on the wheel.   Tick the appropriate box

TRUE   FALSE
☐   ☐

Q19 True or false? It is easier to judge my position from the kerb
when reversing to the right than when reversing to the left.

TRUE   FALSE
☐   ☐

Tick the appropriate box

Q20 Reversing to the right is more dangerous than reversing to the
left because . . .

1 I cannot see as well

2 I am on the wrong side of the road

3 I might get in the way of vehicles emerging from the side road

Which statement is correct? 1, 2 or 3   Answer ☐

Q21 How far down the side road should you reverse before moving
over to the left-hand side?   Which diagram is correct? A or B?

Answer ☐

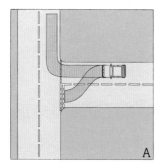

A

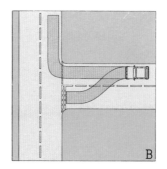

B

ANSWERS ON PAGE 117

Look at the diagrams and decide which is safer.

A Reversing into a side road   B Turning round in the road

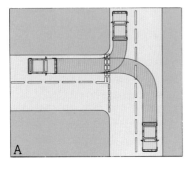

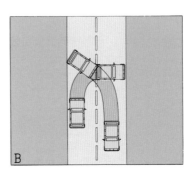

 Answer

 The secret of turning

in the road is to move the vehicle

s_ _ _ _ _ _ and steer

b_ _ _ _ _ _ _ .

Complete the sentence

 True or false? I must

be able to complete the

manoeuvre in three moves:

1 forward, 2 reverse, 3 forward.

TRUE   FALSE

Tick the appropriate box

 Before manoeuvring,

what should you take into

consideration?

Tick the appropriate boxes

 1 The size of your engine

 2 The width of the road

 3 The road camber

 4 The steering circle of your
                    vehicle

 5 Parking restrictions

ANSWERS ON PAGE 117

Q26 Before moving forward, it is important to check a__ __ r__ __ __ __ __ for other road users.   Complete the sentence

Q27 Turning in the road requires proper use of the steering wheel.

Answer the following questions

1 When going forwards, which way should you steer?

Answer ————————————————

2 Before you reach the kerb ahead, what should you do?

Answer ————————————————

3 When reversing, which way should you steer?

Answer ————————————————

4 Before you reach the kerb behind you, what should you do?

Answer ————————————————

5 As you move forward again, which way should you steer to straighten up?

Answer ————————————————

Q28 Reversing is a potentially dangerous manoeuvre. Good observation is essential.   Answer the following questions

1 If you are steering left when reversing, which shoulder should you look over?

Answer ————————————————

2 As you begin to steer to the right, where should you look?

Answer ————————————————

ANSWERS ON PAGES 117-18

When parking between two cars . . .

1 The car is more manoeuvrable when driving forwards

2 The car is more manoeuvrable when reversing

3 There is no difference between going into the space forwards or reversing into it

Which statement is correct? 1, 2 or 3? Answer

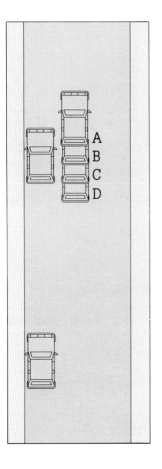

 The diagram shows a car preparing to reverse into a parking space. Which position is the correct one in which to start steering left?

 Answer

Q31 With practice you should be able to park in a gap . . .

1 Your own car length

2 $1\frac{1}{2}$ times your own car length

3 2 times your own car length

4 $2\frac{1}{2}$ times your own car length

 Answer

ANSWERS ON PAGE 118

Use the diagram to help you answer the following questions.

1 Which way would you steer?

Answer ————————————

2 At this point what would you try to line up with the

offside (right-hand side) of your vehicle?

Answer ————————————

3 As you straighten up what do you have to be careful of?

Answer ————————————

4 What do you need to do to straighten up?

Answer ————————————

5 What would you need to do in order to position the vehicle

parallel to the kerb?   Answer ————————————

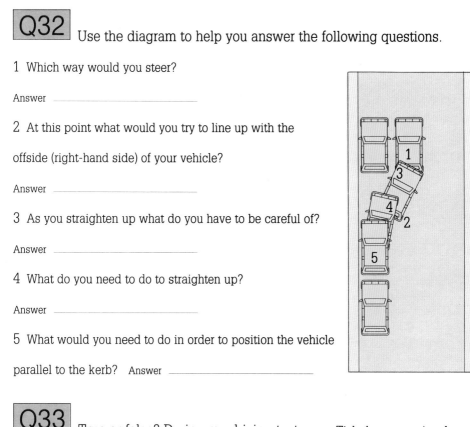

True or false? During my driving test . . .   Tick the appropriate boxes

TRUE   FALSE

☐   ☐   1 I will certainly be asked to perform this manoeuvre

☐   ☐   2 I have to be able to park between two cars

☐   ☐   3 Only the lead car will be present

ANSWERS ON PAGE 118

When carrying out this manoeuvre, where is it important to look?

Answer ————————————

Traffic lights have three lights, red, amber, and green, which change from one to the other in a set order. Number the boxes 1 to 5 to show the correct order. The first one has been filled in to give you a start.

☐ Amber   1 Red   ☐ Red and amber   ☐ Red   ☐ Green

 What do the colours mean?

Fill in the correct colour for each of the following

1 Go ahead if the way is clear.   Colour _____

2 Stop and wait.   Colour _____

3 Stop unless you have crossed the stop line or you are
   so close to it that stopping might cause an accident.   Colour _____

4 Stop and wait at the stop line.   Colour _____

 Which of the following statements are true? Tick the appropriate boxes

On approach to traffic lights you should . . .

☐   1 Speed up to get through before they change

☐   2 Be ready to stop   ANSWERS ON PAGE 118

☐   3 Look out for pedestrians

☐   4 Sound your horn to urge pedestrians to cross quickly

Some traffic lights have green filters. Do they mean . . .

1 You can filter in the direction of the arrow only when the main light

is showing green?

2 You can filter even when the main light is not showing green?   Answer [ ]

 The diagram shows the three lanes at a set of traffic lights.

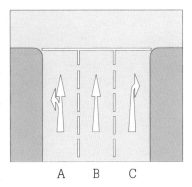

A   B   C

Which lane would you use for . . .

1 Going ahead   Answer _____

2 Turning right   Answer _____

3 Turning left   Answer _____

ANSWERS ON PAGE 118

 At some traffic lights and junctions you will see yellow

criss-cross lines (box junctions). Can you . . .   Tick the appropriate boxes

YES NO

[ ] [ ] 1 Wait within them when going ahead if your exit is not clear?

[ ] [ ] 2 Wait within them when going right if your exit is not clear?

[ ] [ ] 3 Wait within them if there is oncoming traffic stopping you turning right but your exit is clear?

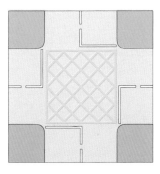

Pedestrians have certain rights of way at pedestrian crossings.

 On approach to a zebra crossing, drivers will notice four features.

Name them

1 _____

2 _____

3 _____

4 _____

 Are these statements about pedestrian crossings true or false?

TRUE FALSE

 1 I cannot park or wait on the zig-zag lines on the approach to a zebra crossing.

 2 I cannot park or wait on the zig-zag lines on either side of the crossing.

 3 I can overtake on the zig-zag lines on the approach to a crossing as long as the other vehicle is travelling slowly.

 4 I must give way to a pedestrian once he/she has stepped on to the crossing.

5 If, on approach to a crossing, I intend to slow down or stop, I should use a slowing-down arm signal.

Tick the appropriate boxes

ANSWERS ON PAGES 118-19

Pelican crossings are light-controlled crossings.

 On approach to a pelican crossing drivers will notice three key features.

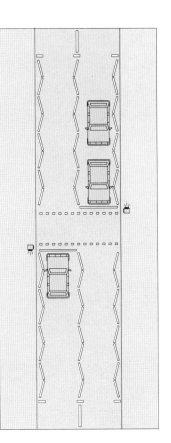

Name them

1 _____

2 _____

3 _____

Q10 If you see a pedestrian at a zebra or pelican crossing carrying a white stick, do you think . . .   Tick the appropriate box

☐ 1 He/she has   ☐ 2 He/she is
     difficulty walking?   visually
                                   handicapped?

Q11 The traffic lights at a pelican crossing have the same meaning as ordinary traffic lights, but they do not have a red and amber phase.

1 What do they show instead of the red and amber phase?   Answer _____

2 What does the light mean?   Answer _____

Q12 What sound is usually heard at a pelican crossing when the green man is shown to pedestrians?

ANSWERS ON PAGE 119

Answer _____

A level crossing is where the road crosses at a railway line. It is potentially dangerous and should be approached with caution.

Q13 Match each traffic sign below with its correct meaning.

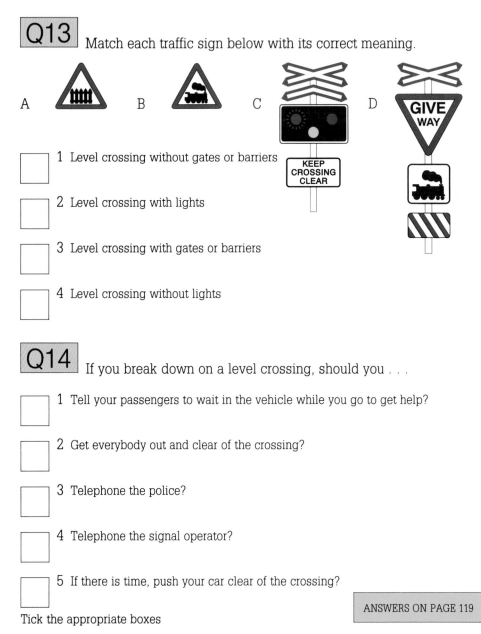

A   B   C   D

1 Level crossing without gates or barriers

2 Level crossing with lights

3 Level crossing with gates or barriers

4 Level crossing without lights

Q14 If you break down on a level crossing, should you . . .

1 Tell your passengers to wait in the vehicle while you go to get help?

2 Get everybody out and clear of the crossing?

3 Telephone the police?

4 Telephone the signal operator?

5 If there is time, push your car clear of the crossing?

Tick the appropriate boxes

ANSWERS ON PAGE 119

One-way systems are where all traffic flows in the same direction.

Q1 Which of these signs means one-way traffic?

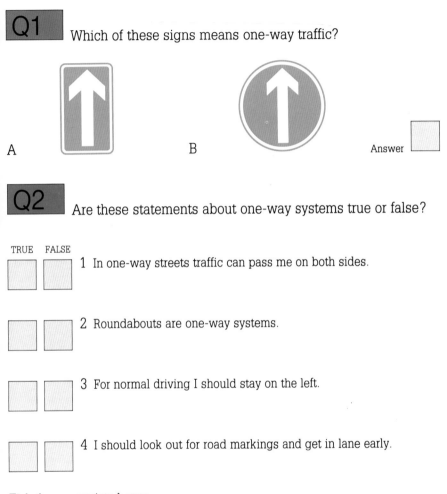

A   B   Answer ☐

Q2 Are these statements about one-way systems true or false?

TRUE   FALSE

☐   ☐   1 In one-way streets traffic can pass me on both sides.

☐   ☐   2 Roundabouts are one-way systems.

☐   ☐   3 For normal driving I should stay on the left.

☐   ☐   4 I should look out for road markings and get in lane early.

Tick the appropriate boxes

ANSWERS ON PAGE 119

As a rule, the more paint on the road, the more important the message.

 Road markings are divided into three categories.

Fill in the missing words

1　Those which give i＿＿＿＿＿＿＿＿＿＿＿＿ .

2　Those which give w＿＿＿＿＿＿＿＿ .

3　Those which give o＿＿＿＿＿ .

ANSWERS ON PAGE 119

 There are two main advantages which road markings have over

other traffic signs. Name them

1 ＿＿＿＿＿＿＿＿＿＿＿＿＿＿＿＿＿＿＿＿＿

2 ＿＿＿＿＿＿＿＿＿＿＿＿＿＿＿＿＿＿＿＿＿

 What do these lines across the road mean?

1　Stop and give way

2　Give priority to traffic coming from the immediate right.

3　Give way to traffic coming from the right.

Answer

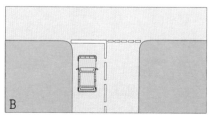

1　Give way to traffic on the major road.

2　Stop at the line and give way to traffic on the major road.

Answer

Q6   What do these lines painted along the road mean?

1 I must not park or wait on the carriageway.

2 I can park between 7pm and 7am

3 I must not overtake.

4 I must not cross the white line except to turn right or in circumstances beyond my control.

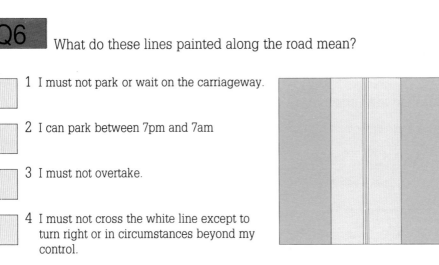

More than one answer may be correct. Tick any boxes you think are appropriate.

Q7   What is the purpose of these hatched markings (chevrons)?

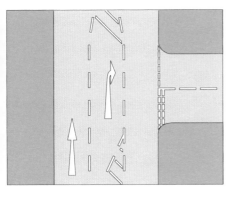

Answer _____

Q8   What does it mean if the chevrons are edged with a solid white line?

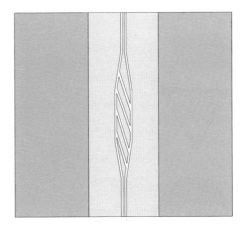

Answer _____

ANSWERS ON PAGE 119

The shape and colour of a sign will help you understand what it means.

 Look at the signs below and say whether each gives an order, a warning or information.

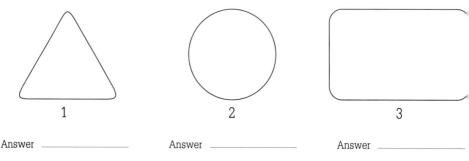

1   2   3

Answer _____   Answer _____   Answer _____

 1 A circular sign with a blue background tells you what you

m_ _ _ do.

2 A circular sign with a red border tells you what you m_ _ _ _ n_ _ do.

Complete the sentences

 What do these signs mean?

1   Answer _____

2   Answer _____

ANSWERS ON PAGE 120

Q12 Some junctions have a stop sign, others have a give way sign.

Complete the sentence

A stop sign is usually placed at a junction where v_ _ _ _ _

is l_ _ _ _ _ _ _

Q13 Information signs are colour-coded.

Match each of the following five types of sign to its colouring

Motorway signs   A White letters on a brown background

Primary routes   B Black letters on a white background

Other routes   C Black letters on a white background with
                     a blue border

Local places   D White letters on a blue background with
                     a white border

Tourists signs   E White letters on a green background,
                     yellow route numbers with a white border

ANSWERS ON PAGE 120

Good observation is vital in today's busy traffic.

Complete the sentence

When using my mirrors I should try to make a mental note of the s_ _ _ _ _,

b_ _ _ _ _ _ _ _ _ and i_ _ _ _ _ _ _ _ _ _ of the driver behind.

 Driving in built-up areas is potentially dangerous.

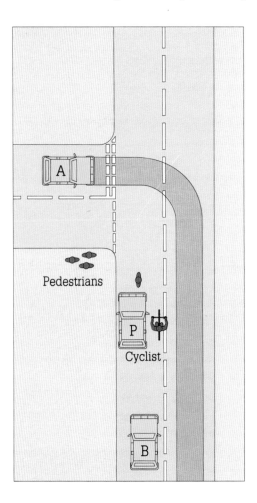

Pedestrians

P

Cyclist

A

B

Look at this diagram

1 What action should the driver of

car A take? List four options

A _____

B _____

C _____

D _____

2 What action should the driver of

car B take? List four options

A _____

B _____

C _____

D _____

ANSWERS ON PAGE 120

Motor cyclists are often less visible than other road users.

Complete this well-known phrase

Think once, think twice, think b_ _ _ .

 When you observe traffic following too close behind you,

would you . . .   Tick the appropriate box

1 Speed up to create a bigger gap?

2 Dab your brake lights to warn the following driver?

3 Keep to a safe speed, and keep checking the behaviour and intentions
of the following driver?

 Some hazards are potential, others are actual and there all the

time, such as a bend in the road.

A Name five more actual hazards

1 _____

2 _____

3 _____

4 _____

5 _____

B Name five potential hazards, such

as a dog off its lead

1 _____

2 _____

3 _____

4 _____

5 _____

ANSWERS ON PAGE 120

One of the features of driving on the open road is taking bends properly.

 As a rule you should be travelling at the correct s_ _ _ _ _ ,

using the correct g_ _ _ _ , and be in the correct p_ _ _ _ _ _ _ _ .

 Should you brake . . .

☐ 1 Before you enter the bend?   ☐ 2 As you enter the bend?

☐ 3 While negotiating the bend?

Tick the appropriate box

 Which way does force push a car on a bend?

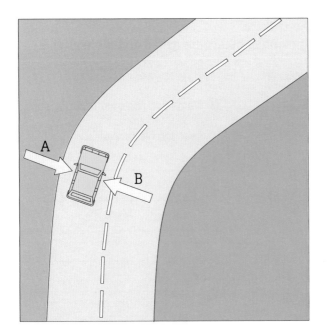

A Inwards

or

B Outwards

Answer ☐

ANSWERS ON PAGE 120

Q9 What happens to the weight of the car when you use the brakes?

A It is thrown forwards B It remains even C It is thrown back Answer

Q10 When you approach a bend, what position should you be in?

A On a right-hand bend I should

keep to the _____

B On a left-hand bend I should

keep to the _____

Complete the sentences

ANSWERS ON PAGE 121

Overtaking is a potentially dangerous manoeuvre.

Q11 Before overtaking, consider whether it is really

n_ _ _ _ _ _ _ _ _ .   Fill in the missing word

Always use the safety routine when overtaking.

Put these actions into their correct sequence by putting the numbers 1 to 7, as seen in

the diagram, in the boxes

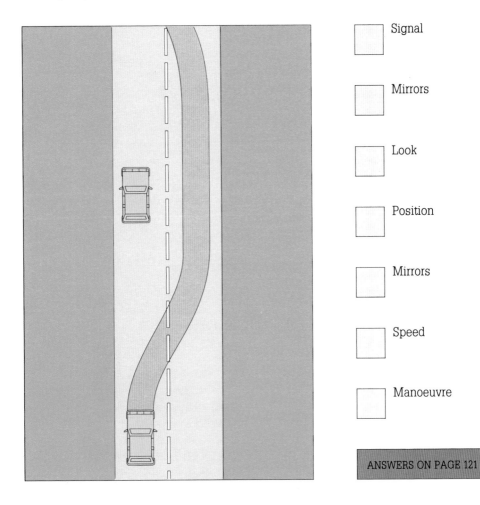

Signal

Mirrors

Look

Position

Mirrors

Speed

Manoeuvre

ANSWERS ON PAGE 121

Q12 What is the minimum amount of clearance you should give a cyclist or motor cyclist?

Answer _____

Q13 There are four situations in which you may, with caution, overtake on the left-hand side of the car in front.   Name them

1 _____

2 _____

3 _____

4 _____

Q14 List four places where it would be dangerous to overtake.

1 _____

2 _____

3 _____

4 _____

ANSWERS ON PAGE 121

Dual carriageways can appear similar to motorways, but there are important differences.

Which of the following statements apply to dual carriageways?

Tick the relevant boxes

1 Reflective studs are not used.

2 Cyclists are allowed.

ANSWERS ON PAGE 121

3 The speed limit is always 60 mph.

4 You cannot turn right to enter or leave a dual carriageway.

5 Milk floats and slow moving farm vehicles are prohibited.

When turning right from a minor road on to a dual carriageway, where would you wait . . .

A When there is a wide central reserve?

Answer _____

B When the central reserve is too narrow for your car?

Answer _____

When travelling at 70 mph on a dual carriageway, which lane would you use?

Answer _____

Q18 What do these signs mean?

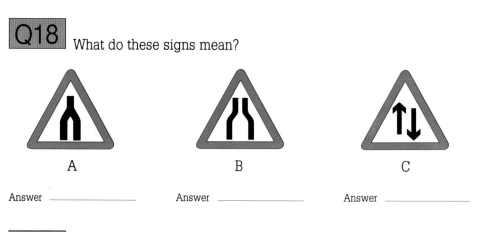

A   B   C

Answer _____   Answer _____   Answer _____

Q19 Which of the above signs would you expect to see on a dual carriageway?

Answer _____

ANSWERS ON PAGE 121

Q1 Cars fitted with automatic transmission select the gear

depending on the road speed and the load on the engine.

They therefore have no c_ _ _ _ _ pedal.

Fill in the missing word

Q2 The advantages of an automatic car are . . .

1 _____

2 _____

Q3 The gear selector has the same function as a manual selector,

but what function do each of the following have?

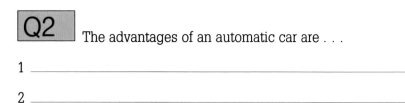

Park _____

Reverse _____

Neutral _____

Drive _____

3rd _____

2nd _____

1st _____

ANSWERS ON PAGE 122

Q4   Automatic cars have a device called a kickdown. Is its function . . .

☐   1   To select a higher gear?

☐   2   To select a lower gear manually?

☐   3   To provide quick acceleration when needed?   Tick the relevant box

Q5   When driving an automatic car, would you select a lower gear . . .

YES   NO

☐ ☐   1   To control speed when going down a steep hill?

☐ ☐   2   To slow the car down in normal driving?

☐ ☐   3   When going uphill?

☐ ☐   4   To overtake, in certain circumstances?

☐ ☐   5   When manoeuvring?

☐ ☐   6   Before stopping?

Tick the appropriate boxes

ANSWERS ON PAGE 122

Q6 An automatic car has two foot pedals, the foot-brake and the accelerator.

For normal driving, which foot would you use . . .

1 For the brake?   Answer _____

2 For the accelerator?   Answer _____

Q7 When driving along using one foot to control both pedals is preferable to using both the left and the right foot. Why?

Answer _____

_____

_____

Q8 Some cars with automatic transmission have a tendency to 'creep'.

Which gears allow the car to creep?

Answer _____

ANSWERS ON PAGE 122

Q9 When driving an automatic car, would you use the handbrake . . .

☐ 1 More than in a manual car?

☐ 2 The same?

☐ 3 Less?   Tick the relevant box

Q10 In which position should the gear selector be when you are

starting the engine?

Answer ——————————————— or ———————————————

Q11 As you approach a bend, an automatic car will sometimes

change up because there is less pressure on the accelerator.

What should you do to prevent this happening?

☐ 1 Slow down before the bend and accelerate gently as you turn.

☐ 2 Brake as you go round the bend.

☐ 3 Brake and accelerate at the same time.

ANSWERS ON PAGE 122

Tick the relevant box

There are many myths and legends surrounding the driving test.

Are the following statements true or false? Tick the relevant boxes

TRUE FALSE

1 The driving test is designed to see whether I can drive around a test route without making any mistakes.

2 The driving test is designed to see whether I can drive safely under various traffic conditions.

3 I do not need to know any highway code.

4 The examiner has a set allocation of passes each week.

5 My knowledge of other motoring matters, for example the cause of skids, may be tested.

 The length of the normal driving test is approximately . . .

1 60 minutes

2 90 minutes

3 35 minutes

Tick the correct box

ANSWERS ON PAGE 122

If, during the test, you do not understand what the examiner says to you, you should take a guess because you must not talk to him or her.

TRUE   FALSE

 Is this statement true or false?   Tick the correct box

 You may have heard people say that it is easier to pass the driving test in certain parts of the country.

YES   NO

 Do you agree with this statement?   Tick the correct box

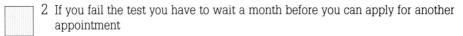 If you fail your test, you can take it again.

Which of the following statements is correct?   Tick the relevant box(es)

 1 If you fail the test, you can apply straight away for another appointment.

2 If you fail the test you have to wait a month before you can apply for another appointment

 3 You can re-take your test, subject to appointment availability, any time.

 4 You have to wait a month before you can re-take the test.

ANSWERS ON PAGES 122-23

Before the practical part of your test, the examiner will test your

eyesight. This is done by asking you to read a number plate at a distance of . . .

 1 30.5 metres (100 feet)

 2 20.5 metres (67 feet)

 3 40.5 metres (133 feet)   Tick the correct box

 What will happen if you fail your eyesight test?

Answer _____

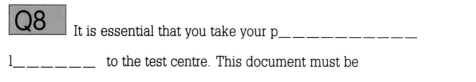 It is essential that you take your p_____

l_____ to the test centre. This document must be

s_____ in ink.   Complete the sentences

The examiner will expect you to drive without making

any mistakes.   Do you think this statement is true or false?

TRUE   FALSE

 Tick the correct box

ANSWERS ON PAGE 123

Is this statement about what you will be asked to do during the test true or false?

I will be asked to perform four set exercises:

1　The emergency stop

2　The turn in the road

3　Reversing into a side road on the right or left

4　Reverse parallel parking

TRUE　　FALSE

 Tick the relevant box

 When reversing, are you allowed to undo your seat belt?

TRUE　　FALSE

 Tick the correct box

 If you fail your test, what will the examiner do?

1 _____

2 _____

ANSWERS ON PAGE 123

When you have passed your driving test, what are

you entitled to do?

1 _____

2 _____

3 _____

 I have within the last month passed my test.

Can I supervise a learner driver?

YES   NO

Tick the correct box

 When you pass your test, where should you send

your pass certificate?

Answer _____

 While you are waiting for your full licence to be sent to you,

can you drive legally?

YES   NO

Tick the correct box

ANSWERS ON PAGE 123

It is recommended that you take further tuition once you have passed your test, especially on motorway driving.

As a learner driver you will not have experienced the special r_ _ _ _ that apply on the motorway and the h_ _ _ _   s_ _ _ _ _ of the other traffic.

Complete the sentence

 While taking your driving test, you should drive . . .

1 Especially carefully, keeping about 5 mph below the speed limit

2 As you would normally drive with your instructor

3 With confidence, keeping at or just over the speed limit, to show that you can really drive.

Tick the relevant box

 Can you take a driving test if you are deaf?

YES   FALSE

Tick the correct box

ANSWERS ON PAGE 123

The driving test ensures that all drivers reach a minimum standard.

 Do you think that learning to drive ends with passing the test?

YES   NO

 Tick the correct box

 What knowledge and skills are not necessarily assessed in the present driving test?   List three

1 _____

2 _____

3 _____

 Which of these statements do you think best describes advanced driving?   Tick the relevant box

 1 Advanced driving is learning to handle your car to its maximum performance.

 2 Advanced driving is learning to drive defensively with courtesy and consideration to others.

3 Advanced driving is learning to drive fast.

ANSWERS ON PAGE 123

Some people have difficulty in driving at night.

Who would you expect, in general, to experience most difficulties?

Tick the relevant box

☐ 1 Older people

☐ 2 Younger people

 Once you have passed your driving test, your licence is usually

valid until you reach __ __ years of age. Complete the sentence

 There are particular circumstances under which you are required

to take a driving test again. Name them

Answer _____

_____

ANSWERS ON PAGE 124

Q7 Motorways are designed to enable traffic to travel faster in

greater safety. Compared to other roads, are they statistically . . .

☐ 1 Safer   ☐ 2 Less safe?   ☐ 3 No different?

Tick the relevant box

Q8 Are the following groups allowed on the motorway?

YES NO

☐ ☐ 1 Provisional licence holders

☐ ☐ 2 Motor cycles over 50cc

☐ ☐ 3 Pedestrians

☐ ☐ 4 HGV learner drivers

☐ ☐ 5 Newly qualified drivers with less than three months' experience

☐ ☐ 6 Motor cycles under 125cc

☐ ☐ 7 Cyclists

Tick the relevant boxes

ANSWERS ON PAGE 124

There are some routine checks you should carry out on your car before driving on the motorway. Name four of them

1 _____ 2 _____

3 _____ 4 _____

 On the motorway, if something falls from either your own or another vehicle, should you . . .

☐ 1 Flash your headlights to inform other drivers?

☐ 2 Pull over, put your hazard warning lights on and quickly run on to the motorway to collect the object?

☐ 3 Pull over on to the hard shoulder, use the emergency telephone to call the police?

☐ 4 Flag another motorist down to get help?

 Which colour do you associate with motorway signs?

☐ 1 Black lettering on a white background

☐ 2 White lettering on a green background

☐ 3 White lettering on a blue background

Tick the correct box

ANSWERS ON PAGE 124

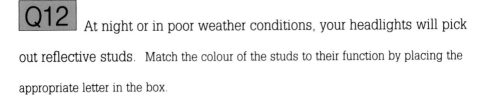 At night or in poor weather conditions, your headlights will pick out reflective studs. Match the colour of the studs to their function by placing the appropriate letter in the box.

☐ Amber	A Marks the edge of the hard shoulder
☐ Red	B Marks the edge of the central reservation
☐ Green	C Marks lane lines
☐ White	D Marks exits and entrances

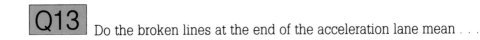 Do the broken lines at the end of the acceleration lane mean . . .

☐ 1 The edge of the carriageway?

☐ 2 Other traffic should let you in?

☐ 3 Give way to traffic already on the carriageway?   Tick the correct box

 If you see congestion ahead, is it legal to use your hazard warning lights to warn drivers behind you?   Tick the correct box

YES   NO
☐   ☐

ANSWERS ON PAGE 124

Q15 What is the most common cause of accidents on motorways?

☐ 1 Vehicles breaking down   ☐ 2 Drivers falling asleep

☐ 3 Drivers travelling too fast, too close to the vehicle in front   ☐ 4 Fog   Tick the correct box

Q16 Are the following statements true or false?

I can use the hard shoulder . . .

TRUE   FALSE

☐ ☐ 1 To take a short break

ANSWERS ON PAGE 124

☐ ☐ 2 To stop and read a map

☐ ☐ 3 To allow the children to stretch their legs

☐ ☐ 4 To pull over in an emergency

☐ ☐ 5 To answer a phone call   Tick the relevant box

Q17 In normal driving on the motorway, you should overtake . . .

☐ 1 On the right   ☐ 2 On the left

☐ 3 On either side

Tick the correct box

Driving at night can cause problems.

ANSWERS ON PAGE 124

 Which of these statements do you think is correct?

Tick the relevant box

☐ 1 Street lighting and my car's headlights mean that I can see just as well as in the daylight. Therefore driving at night is just like driving in the daylight.

☐ 2 At night I have to rely on my car's headlights and any additional lighting. Therefore I cannot see as far or drive as fast as in the daylight.

 At dusk and dawn what action should you take to compensate for driving a dark coloured car?

Answer ——————————————————————————————————————

 When driving after dark in a built-up area, should you use . . .

 1 Dipped headlights?

 2 Side or dim-dipped lights?   Tick the correct box

 The Highway Code says you should not use your horn in a built-up area between 11.30pm and 7am.

What is the exception to that rule?

Answer ——————————————————————————————————————

The diagram below illustrates two vehicles parked at night on a two-way road. Which one is parked correctly?

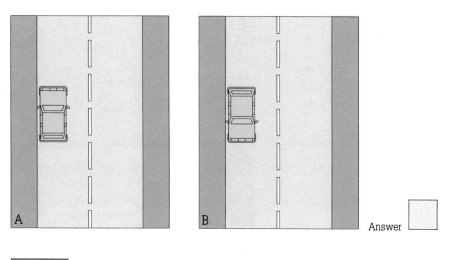

A

B

Answer

Q23 Certain groups of road users are particularly vulnerable at night.

Name two of them

1 _____ 2 _____

Q24 Under what circumstances would you use dipped headlights

during the day? Answer _____

S___ and b__ s____. Complete the sentence

Q25 When you are waiting at a junction after dark, your brake lights

might d_____ the driver behind. It is better to

use your h_____. Complete the sentences

ANSWERS ON PAGES 125-26

Certain weather conditions can create hazardous driving conditions in the summer as well as in the winter.

 Which of the following causes greatest danger to drivers?

Tick the correct box

  1 Snow   □ 2 Ice

□ 3 Heavy rain   □ 4 Not being able to see properly

 In wet weather conditions your tyres can lose their grip.

You should allow at least d_ _ _ _ _ _ the distance between you and the car in front that you allow on a dry road.   *Fill in the missing word*

Q28 In very wet conditions there is a danger of a build-up of water between your tyres and the road.

This is called a _ _ _ _ _ _ _ _ _ _ _ _ .   *Fill in the missing word*

ANSWERS ON PAGE 125

How should you deal with floods?

Tick the correct box

☐ 1 Drive through as fast as possible to avoid stopping

☐ 2 Drive through slowly in 1st gear, slipping the clutch to keep the engine speed high

☐ 3 Drive through in the highest gear possible, slipping the clutch to keep the engine speed high

 Will less tread on your tyres . . .　　　Tick the correct box

☐ 1 Increase your braking distance?　　☐ 2 Decrease your braking distance?

 When the tyres lose contact with the road, the steering will feel

v＿＿＿＿　l＿＿＿＿＿.　　　　　Complete the sentence

 After you have driven through a flood, should you check . . .

☐ 1 Your speedometer?　　　　　　☐ 2 Your brakes?

☐ 3 Your oil?

ANSWERS ON PAGE 125

Tick the correct box

Q33 There are certain key precautions you should take when driving

in fog. Complete the following sentences

1 S_ _ _ _ d_ _ _ _ .

2 Ensure you are able to s_ _ _ _ within the distance you can see

to be clear.

3 Use your w_ _ _ _ _ _ _ _ _ _ _ w_ _ _ _ _ _.

4 Use your d_ _ _ _ _ _ _ and your h_ _ _ _ _ _ _ r_ _ _ _

w_ _ _ _ _ _ _ _ _ _ _.

Q34 Under what circumstances should you use your rear fog lights?

When visibility is less than _____ metres/yards

Fill in the correct number

Q35 When you are following another vehicle in fog, should you . . .

☐ 1 Follow closely behind because it will help you see where you are going?

☐ 2 Leave plenty of room between you and the vehicle in front?

Tick the correct box

ANSWERS ON PAGE 125

When you are following another vehicle in fog, should you use . . .

☐ 1 Main beam headlights?   ☐ 2 Dipped headlights?

Tick the correct box

 Extra precautions are needed when dealing with a junction in fog.

Complete the following sentences

1 Open your w_ _ _ _ _ _ and switch off your a_ _ _ _ _ s_ _ _ _ _ _.

   L_ _ _ _ _ for other vehicles.

2 Signal e_ _ _ _ _ .

3 Use your b_ _ _ _ _ _. The light will a_ _ _ _ _ following vehicles.

4 Use your h_ _ _ _ if you think it will w_ _ _ _ other road users.

Q38   Is the following statement about anti-lock brakes true or false?

TRUE   FALSE

☐   ☐   Anti-lock brakes will stop me skidding when driving on snow or ice.

Tick the correct box

ANSWERS ON PAGE 125

When driving in snow or ice you should gently test your

b_ _ _ _ _ _ from time to time.   Fill in the missing word

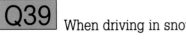 In order to slow down when driving on snow or ice you should . . .

1 Use your brakes g_ _ _ _ _ _.

2 Get into a l_ _ _ _ _ g_ _ _ earlier than normal.

3 Allow your speed to d_ _ _ _ and use your b_ _ _ _ _ _ gently and early.

Fill in the missing words

Q41 On snow or ice braking distances can increase by . . .

☐ 1 10 times

☐ 2 5 times

ANSWERS ON PAGE 125

☐ 3 20 times

☐ 4 15 times   Tick the correct box

Q42 When going downhill in snow, what would you do to help you

slow down?

Answer _____

Q43 When cornering in snow or ice, what should you avoid doing?

Answer _____

Q44 How can you reduce the risk of wheel spin?

Answer _____

Q45 Three important factors cause a skid.   Name them

1 _____

2 _____

3 _____

Q46 Some everyday driving actions, especially in poor weather, can increase the risk of skidding.

Fill in the missing words

1 S_ _ _ _ _ _ down.

2 S_ _ _ _ _ _ _ up.

3 T_ _ _ _ _ _ corners.

4 Driving u_ _ _ _ _ _ and d_ _ _ _ _ _ _ _.

ANSWERS ON PAGE 125

All vehicles need routine attention and maintenance to keep them in good working order. Neglecting maintenance can be costly and dangerous.

 With which of these statements do you agree? Tick the relevant box

1 Allowing the fuel gauge to drop too low is bad for the engine.

2 In modern cars the fuel level makes little difference.

 What do you put into the engine to lubricate the moving parts?

Answer _____

 How frequently should you check your oil level? Tick the correct box

1 Once a month

2 Once a year

ANSWERS ON PAGE 126

3 Every time you fill up with fuel

 The engine is often cooled by a mixture of w_ _ _ _ _   and

a_ _ _ _ -f_ _ _ _ _ _ . Some engines are a_ _ cooled.

Complete the sentences

Part 15

Vehicle care 97

Q5 How frequently should you test your brakes? Tick the correct box

☐ 1 Daily ☐ 2 Monthly ☐ 3 Weekly

☐ 4 When I use them

ANSWERS ON PAGE 126

Q6 Incorrectly adjusted headlamps can cause d_ _ _ _ _ _ to other road users.

Complete the sentence

Q7 All headlamps, indicators and brake lights should be kept in good working order.

It is also important that they are kept c_ _ _ _ _.

Fill in the missing word

Q8 Tyres should be checked for u_ _ _ _ _ _ wear and tyre walls for b_ _ _ _ _ _ and c_ _ _ _ .

Complete the sentence

Q9 The legal requirement for tread depth is not less than . . .

☐ 1 1.4mm ☐ 2 1.6mm ☐ 3 2mm

Tick the correct box

Q10 What should you do if your brakes feel slack or spongy?

Answer _____

It is important that all road users know what to do in the case of breakdown, accident or emergency. A lack of knowledge could put lives at risk.

 Vehicle breakdowns could result from . . .

1 N_ _ _ _ _ _ _ of the vehicle

2 Lack of r_ _ _ _ _ _ _   c_ _ _ _ _ _

3 Little or no p_ _ _ _ _ _ _ _ _ _ _ _ _   maintenance

4 A_ _ _ _ _ of the vehicle

Fill in the missing words

 It is advisable to carry a warning triangle.

1   On a straight road how far back should it be placed?

☐ 50m/yds   ☐ 200m/yds   ☐ 150m/yds

Tick the correct box

2 On a dual carriageway, how far back should it be placed? At least . . .

☐ 200m/yds   ☐ 150m/yds   ☐ 400m/yds

Tick the correct box

ANSWERS ON PAGE 126

If you use a warning triangle, is it worth putting your hazard lights on as well?

YES   NO

 Tick the correct box

 If your vehicle breaks down on a motorway, should you . . .

 1 Gently brake, put your hazard lights on and seek assistance?

2 Pull over on to the central reservation as far to the right as possible?

3 Pull over safely on to the hard shoulder as far away from the carriageway as possible?

Tick the correct box

 If your vehicle has broken down on the motorway, should you tell your passengers to . . .

 1 Stay in the vehicle while you seek assistance?

 2 Wait by the car on the hard shoulder but watch out for other vehicles?

 3 Get out of the vehicle and wait on the embankment away from the hard shoulder?

ANSWERS ON PAGE 126

Tick the correct box

The marker posts at the side of all
motorways have a picture of a telephone handset.

How can you tell which way to walk to reach

the nearest telephone?

Answer _____

_____

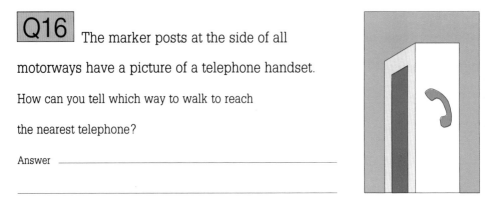

Q17 When you use the emergency telephone on a motorway, what
will the operator ask you?

1 _____

2 _____

3 _____

4 _____

Q18 Disabled drivers cannot easily get to an emergency telephone.
How can they summon help?

1 _____

2 _____

ANSWERS ON PAGE 126

If you break down when travelling alone, there are three things

you are advised NOT to do.   Complete these sentences

1 Do not ask p_ _ _ _ _ _ _ _   m_ _ _ _ _ _ _ _ _ _   for help.

2 Do not accept help from anyone you d_ n_ _ k_ _ _ _ (except the

emergency services or a breakdown service).

3 Do not l_ _ _ _ _ your vehicle l_ _ _ _ _ _ than necessary.

 If I am first or one of the first to arrive at the scene of

an accident, should I . . .

TRUE   FALSE

1 Always move injured people away from vehicles?

2 Tell the ambulance personnel or paramedics what I think is wrong
with those injured?

3 Give casualties something warm to drink?

4 Switch off hazard warning lights?

5 Switch off vehicle engines?

6 Inform the police of the accident?

ANSWERS ON PAGE 126

Tick the appropriate boxes

If you are involved in an accident, what MUST you do?

Answer _____

 If you are involved in an accident and nobody is injured, do you have to call the police?

YES   NO

Tick the correct box

 What information do you need to exchange if you are involved in an accident?

1 _____

2 _____

3 _____

4 _____

5 _____

ANSWERS ON PAGES 126-27

If you thought you had a fire in your car's engine, what action would you take?

1 _____

2 _____

3 _____

 There are three items of emergency equipment it is wise to carry in your car.

1 F_ _ _ _   a_ _ kit.

2 F_ _ _ _   e_ _ _ _ _ _ _ _ _ _ _ _ _ .

3 W_ _ _ _ _ _ _ _   t_ _ _ _ _ _ _ _ .

Fill in the missing words

 When you rejoin a motorway from the hard shoulder, should you . . .

☐ 1 Signal right and join when there is a safe gap?

 2 Keep your hazard lights on and drive down the hard shoulder until there is a safe gap?

 3 Use the hard shoulder to build up speed and join the carriageway when safe?

Tick the correct box

ANSWERS ON PAGE 127

Fuel combustion causes waste products.

One of these is a gas called c_ _ _ _ _ _   d_ _ _ _ _ _ _ . This is a major

cause of the g_ _ _ _ _ _ _ _ _ _ effect.

Complete the sentences

 How much does transport contribute to the production of carbon

dioxide in this country (expressed as a percentage of the total production)?

☐ 1 10 per cent   ☐ 2 25 per cent

☐ 3 50 per cent   ☐ 4 20 per cent

 The MOT test checks the roadworthiness of a vehicle.

Does it include an exhaust emission test?

YES   NO
☐   ☐   Tick the correct box

 A catalytic convertor stops the emission of carbon dioxide.

TRUE   FALSE
☐   ☐

Tick the correct box

ANSWERS ON PAGE 127

Q31 Which is more environmentally friendly?

☐ 1 A petrol engine with a catalytic convertor   ☐ 2 A diesel engine

Tick the correct box

ANSWERS ON PAGE 127

Q32 Which uses up more fuel?

☐ 1 A car travelling at 50mph   ☐ 2 A car travelling at 70mph

Tick the correct box

Q33 Which is environmentally less harmful?

☐ 1 Leaded fuel   ☐ 2 Unleaded fuel

Tick the correct box

Q34 There are some measures car drivers can take to help reduce damage to the environment.   List five

1 _____

2 _____

3 _____

4 _____

5 _____

Before buying a used car it is best to decide what you want the car for and how much you can afford.

 There are three main sources of supply for used vehicles.

You can buy from a d _ _ _ _ _ _ , at an a _ _ _ _ _ _ _ or

p _ _ _ _ _ _ _ _ _ _ .   Complete the sentence

 When reading a glowing description of a used car, what should you first consider?

Answer _____

 Are these statements about buying a used car through a dealer or at an auction true or false?

TRUE   FALSE

1 It is often cheaper to buy a car at an auction than through a dealer.

2 I have the same legal rights when I buy at an auction as when I buy from a dealer.

3 I should always read the terms and conditions of trade before I buy a car at an auction.

4 The best way to select a used car dealer is by recommendation.

ANSWERS ON PAGE 127

Tick the appropriate boxes

Q38 Cars bought through a dealer often have a warranty.

What should you check?

1 _____

2 _____

Q39 When you test drive a vehicle, you should make sure that it is

t_ _ _ _ , has a current M_ _ certificate (if applicable) and that all

i_ _ _ _ _ _ _ _ requirements are complied with.

Complete the sentence

Q40 There are some important items that you should check on before

you buy a used car.   List three

1 _____

2 _____

3 _____

Q41 Do you think the following statement is true or false?

It is advisable to have my vehicle examined by a competent and unbiased expert

before I buy.

TRUE   FALSE

☐   ☐

ANSWERS ON PAGES 127-28

Tick the correct box

Particular difficulties are encountered when towing a caravan or trailer. There are some very good courses which will help master the skills required.

 People can underestimate the length of the total combination of car and caravan or trailer. Is the overall length usually . . .

☐ 1 Twice the length of a normal car?	☐ 2 Three times the length of a normal car?

Tick the correct box

 What additional fixtures should you attach to your car to help you see more clearly?

Answer _____

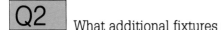 When towing you will need more distance than normal to overtake. Is it . . .

☐ 1 Twice the normal distance?	☐ 2 Three times the normal distance?
☐ 3 Four times the normal distance?	Tick the correct box

 A device called a s_ _ _ _ _ _ _ _ _ _ will make the combination safer to handle.

Fill in the missing word

ANSWERS ON PAGE 128

Q5 The stability of the caravan will depend on how you load it.
Should heavy items be loaded . . . Tick correct box

☐ 1 At the front? ☐ 2 At the rear? ☐ 3 Over the axle(s)?

Q6 There are special restrictions for vehicles which are towing.

A What is the speed limit on a dual carriageway? Tick the correct box

☐ 1 50mph ☐ 2 60mph ☐ 3 70mph

B What is the speed limit on a single carriageway? Tick the correct box

☐ 1 40mph ☐ 2 50mph ☐ 3 60mph

Q7 There are some important checks you should make before
starting off. List four

1 _____ 2 _____

3 _____ 4 _____

Q8 If you decide to stop to take a break, before allowing anyone to
enter the caravan you should lower the j_ _ _ _ _ _ w_ _ _ _ _ and

c_ _ _ _ _ _ s_ _ _ _ _ _ _ _ _.

Fill in the missing words

ANSWERS ON PAGE 128

Many people now take their car abroad or hire a vehicle when on holiday.

Q9 Motoring organisations, such as The Automobile Association, can help you plan and organise your trip.

The AA can provide advice on travel and v_ _ _ _ _ _ _ insurance. They will also help you to organise the d_ _ _ _ _ _ _ _ _ that you will need.

Fill in the missing words

Q10 Before venturing on to the Continent, you should always . . .

1 Plan the r_ _ _ _ _ you wish to take.

2 Know the local m_ _ _ _ _ _ _ _ r_ _ _ _ _ _ _ _ _ _ _ .

Complete the sentences

Q11 It is essential that your vehicle should be checked thoroughly.

List four of the routine checks you should make.

1 _____

2 _____

3 _____

4 _____

ANSWERS ON PAGE 128

Q12 In most European countries you are advised to carry your

d_ _ _ _ _ _ _   l_ _ _ _ _ _ _   on you.   Complete the sentence

Q13 What do the letters I D P stand for?

Answer _____

Q14 Where might you need an I D P ?

Answer _____

Q15 In most European countries what age do you have to be to drive?

☐ 1 21   ☐ 2 18   ☐ 3 16

                                               Tick the correct box

Q16 Some European countries can require you to carry additional

emergency equipment.

List four of the items you are recommended to carry

1 _____

2 _____

3 _____

4 _____

ANSWERS ON PAGE 128

Part 1

Introduction to learning to drive
Questions on pages 10-11

A1

A current, signed, full or provisional licence for the category of vehicle that you are driving

A2

examinations register

A3

21 years old
three years

A4

To the front and rear. It is important not to place them in windows where they could restrict good vision.

A5

True

A6

You should have answered No to all the questions.

A7

Yes. This should be the ambition of every driver.

Adjusting your driving position
Question on page 12

A8

1 handbrake
2 doors
3 seat
4 head restraint
5 mirrors
6 seat belt

Introduction to vehicle controls
Questions on pages 13 - 14

A9

The handbrake	E
The driving mirrors	D
The gear lever	F
The clutch	G
The steering wheel	A
The foot-brake	B
The accelerator gas	C

A10

The foot-brake	R
The clutch	L
The accelerator	R

A11

1 False. You will need one hand to change gear or use other controls.
2 True
3 False. The best position is a quarter to three or ten to two.
4 False. It is safest to feed the wheel through your hands.
5 True
6 True

A12

The direction indicators	B
Dipped beam	A
Main beam	D
Rear fog lamp	C
Horn	E
Hazard lights	F

Part 2

Moving off
Questions on page 15

A1

A	1
B	5
C	3
D	2
E	6
F	4
G	7
H	8
I	9

Stopping (normally)
Question on page 16

A 1
B 3
C 2
D 4
E 6
F 5
G 8
H 7
I 9

Gear changing
Questions on pages 17 - 20

1st gear

5th, or 4th if the car has a 4-speed gear box

Usually 2nd gear, but 1st if you need to go very slowly or 3rd if the corner is sweeping and you can take it safely at a higher speed

engine
vehicle
sound
when

A 1
B 3
C 2
D 4
E 5

1 False. This will cause the engine to labour.
2 False. It is good practice to use the brakes to slow the car down. Using the transmission causes wear and tear which can be very costly. Also, the brakes are more effective.
3 False
4 True
5 False. It is good practice to miss out the unwanted gears and select the gear most appropriate to your road speed.

1

1 Don't
2 Don't
3 Do
4 Do
5 Do
6 Don't
7 Don't
8 Don't

Steering
Questions on page 21

A, except in a few cars fitted with four-wheel steering (in which case all four wheels will move)

A

B

B

Road positioning
Questions on page 22

C, well to the left but not too close to the kerb

B. Avoid swerving in and out. It is unnecessary and confuses other drivers.

Clutch control
Questions on page 23

A

biting

1 Yes
2 Yes
3 No
4 Yes
5 No

Junctions
Questions on pages 24 - 27

two or more roads

A T Junction
B Y Junction
C Roundabout
D Staggered crossroads
E Crossroads

1 E
2 C

3 B
4 D
5 A

A 1
B 3

1 Mirrors
2 Signal
3 Position
4 Speed
5 Look

assess
decide
act

A

B

D

1 mirrors,
   position
2 signal
3 safe
4 safe
   distance
5 overtake

Crossroads
Question on page 28

A 3 Crossroads. Priority for traffic on the major road. Never assume other drivers will give you priority.
B 1 Unmarked crossroads
C 2 Crossroads with give way lines at the end of your road. Give way to traffic on the major road.

Roundabouts
Questions on pages 29 - 30

C

1 Left
2 Left
3 Right. Remember to use the MSM routine before signalling left to turn off.

1 Left
2 Going ahead
3 Right

mirrors,
signal,
position,
speed,
look

2

Parking (on the road)
Questions on page 31

1 safe
2 convenient
3 legal

Cars 1,2,3,6

Passing stationary vehicles and obstructions
Questions on pages 32 - 33

2

2, even though the obstruction is on the right. Where safe, when travelling downhill be prepared to give priority to vehicles (especially heavy vehicles) that are coming uphill.

Meeting and crossing the path of other vehicles
Questions on pages 34 - 35

1 True
2 False. Always consider whether it is safe. Are there dangers the other driver cannot see? Remember, flashing headlamps has the same meaning as sounding the horn. it is a warning: 'I am here!' Sometimes it is taken to mean: 'I am here and I am letting you pass.'
3 True

1 Yes
2 Yes
3 No
4 Yes
5 Yes
6 Yes
7 Yes

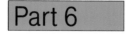

Stopping in an emergency
Questions on pages 36 - 37

1 True
2 True
3 True
4 False
5 False. Looking in the mirror should not be necessary. You should know what is behind you.
6 False
7 True
8 True

pump
1 maximum
2 lock
3 quickly

steer
brake
pump
pressure
1 False. Other elements beyond braking can cause skidding e.g. acceleration or going too fast into a bend.
2 False. Although you may stop in a shorter distance, you still need to leave the correct distance to allow yourself time to react and vehicles behind you time to stop.

Stopping distances
Questions on pages
38 - 39

1 No
2 Yes
3 Yes
4 No

1/2 second

1 23 metres/75 feet
2 15 metres/50 feet
3 96 metres/315 feet

longer
more

breaks
two second

Moving off at an angle
Question on page 40

1 False. You should

check your mirrors and
blindspot before moving out.
Keep alert for other traffic as
you pull out and stop if
necessary.
2 True
3 False. Move out slowly
and carefully.
4 True. The closer you are,
the greater the angle.
5 True. As you move out,
you are likely to move on to
the right-hand side of the
road and into conflict with
oncoming vehicles.
6 False. You should signal
only if it helps or warns other
road users. Signalling gives
you no right to pull out.

Moving off uphill
Question on page 41

1 True
2 False. Using the gas
pedal will not move the car
forwards.
3 False. As your feet
will be using the clutch
pedal and the gas pedal
you need to use the
handbrake to stop the car
rolling back.
4 True
5 True
6 True
7 True

Moving off downhill
Question on page 42

1 True
2 False. Almost
certainly you will need
to use the foot-brake.
3 False. It is often
better to move off in 2nd
gear.
4 True. This will stop
the car rolling forwards.
5 True
6 False. You will
need to have your foot
on the foot-brake to stop
the car rolling forwards.

Approaching junctions uphill and downhill
Question on page 43

The following
statements are correct:
1,4,5,6,7

Reversing
Questions on pages
44 - 45

safe
convenient
law

1 False
2 False
3 True
4 True

A

1,4

A To the left
B To the right

observation

**Reversing into
a side road
on the left**
Questions on pages
46 - 47

3

1 True
2 False
3 True

4

C

Left

The front of the car will
swing out to the right.

1 True
2 False
3 True

pedestrians
road users
stop

**Reversing into a side
road on the right**
Questions on pages 48 - 49

True

B

2

True.   You may need to
place your left hand at 12
o'clock and lower your
right hand.

True

2

B

Turning in the road
Questions on pages
50 - 51

A

slowly briskly

False,   but you should try
to complete the manoeuvre
in as few moves as
possible.

2,3,4

all round

A27

1 Right
2 Steer briskly left
3 Left
4 Steer briskly right
5 Right

A28

1 Left
2 Over your right shoulder to where the car is going

Reverse parallel parking
Questions on pages 52 - 53

A29

2

A30

C , in line with the rear of the parked vehicle

A31

2

A32

1 To the left
2 The nearside headlamp of the vehicle towards which you are reversing
3 Clipping the rear offside of the lead car
4 Take off the left lock
5 Steer to the right and then take off the

right lock as you get straight

A33

1 False
2 False
3 True. You will be expected to be able to complete the exercise within approximately two car lengths.

A34

All round, particularly for pedestrians and oncoming vehicles

Part 9

Traffic lights and yellow box junctions
Questions on pages 54 - 55

A1

1 red
2 red and amber
3 green
4 amber
5 red

A2

1 green
2 red and amber
3 amber
4 red

A3

1 False
2 True
3 True
4 False.
Pedestrians who are already crossing have priority.

A4

2

A5

1 Lane A or B
2 Lane C
3 Lane A

A6

1 No ⌉
2 No ⌋ If your exit is blocked you should not enter a yellow box junction.
3 Yes

Pedestrian crossings
Questions on pages 56 - 57

A7

1 Zig-zag lines
2 Flashing yellow beacons on both sides of the road
3 Black and white stripes on the crossing
4 A give way line

1 True
2 True. You must
not park or wait on the zig-zag
lines on either side of the
crossing.
3 False. You must not
overtake on the zig-zag lines on
approach to the crossing.
4 True
5 True. A slowing down arm
signal should be used. It helps
pedestrians understand what
you intend to do. They cannot
see your brake lights.

1 Traffic lights
2 Zig-zag lines
3 A white stop line

2 A white stick means
the pedestrian is visually
handicapped. A white stick with
two red reflector bands means
the pedestrian may be deaf as
well as visually handicapped.

1 Flashing amber
2 You must give way to
pedestrians on the crossing,
but if it is clear you may go on.

A bleeping tone. This sounds
when the red light shows to
drivers and helps visually
handicapped
pedestrians know
when it is safe to cross.

Level crossings
Questions on page 58

A13

A 3
B 1
C 2
D 4

A14

2
4
5

Part 10

One-way systems
Questions on page 59

A1

A is the correct
sign for a one-way
street.
B tells you 'Ahead
only'.

A2

1 True
2 True
3 True
4 True

Road markings
Questions on pages
60 - 61

information
warnings
orders

1 They can be seen
when other signs
may be hidden
2 They give a
continuing message

A 2
B 2

1,4

They are used
to separate
potentially dangerous
streams
of traffic.

You must not enter
the hatched area.

Traffic signs
Questions on pages
62 - 63

1 Warning
2 Order
3 Information

1 must
2 must not

1 You must give way
to traffic on the major
road. Delay your entry
until it is safe to join the
major road.
2 You must stop (even
if the road is clear). Wait
until you can enter the
new road safely.

vision is limited

Motorway signs   D
Primary routes   E
Other routes   B
Local places   C
Tourist signs   A

Part 11

Road observation
Questions on pages
64 - 65

speed
behaviour
intentions

1 Observe that the view
into the new road is
restricted.
The driver should . . .
Move forward slowly, to get
a better view.
Note the pedestrians who
may walk in front of or
behind car A.
Note the pedestrian waiting
to cross.
Allow the cyclist to pass.
Once in a position to see car
B, stop and give way.
2 Observe that the parked
car restricts the view into
and out of the side road.
The driver should . . .
Slow down on approach to
parked car P.
Take up position to gain a
better view and be more
visible to car A and the
pedestrian.
Slow down in case the
pedestrian walks out from
behind the parked car P.
Consider signal to pass
parked car P.
Look carefully into minor
road. Note the actions of car
A. Be prepared to stop.

bike

3, but dabbing the
brakes may encourage
the driver to drop back

A
1 Junctions
2 Hump-back
bridges
3 Concealed
entrances
4 Dead ground
5 Narrow lanes
B
1 Children playing
2 Horses
3 Pedestrians
4 Especially elderly
and young cyclists
5 Other vehicles

**On the open road
(dealing with
bends)**
Questions on pages
66 - 67

speed
gear
position

1

B

A

A   On a right-hand
bend keep to the left.
This will help to
improve your view.
B   On a left-hand
bend keep to the
centre of the lane.
Do not move to the
centre of the road to
get a better view.
A vehicle travelling
in the opposite
direction may
be taking the
bend wide.

Overtaking
Questions on pages
68 -69

necessary
1   Mirrors
2   Position
3   Speed
4   Look
5   Mirrors
6   Signal
7   Manoeuvre

About the width of a
small car, more in
windy or poor
weather conditions

1   The vehicle in front is
signalling and positioned
to turn right
2   You are using the
correct lane to turn left at a
junction
3   Traffic is moving slowly
in queues and the traffic
on the right is moving
more slowly than you are
4   You are in a one-way
street

1   On approach to a
junction
2   The brow of a hill
3   The approach to a bend
4   Where there is dead
ground   NB These are
examples. Be guided by
The Highway Code

Dual carriageways
Questions on pages
70 - 71

2   Statements 1,3, 4 and 5
do not apply:
1   Reflective studs are
used on some dual
carriageways.
3   The speed limit is
subject to local conditions
and may vary from 40mph
up to the national speed
limit.
4   You can turn right on to
and off dual carriageways

unlike motorways, where
all traffic enters and leaves
on the left.
5   You may find slow
moving vehicles
sometimes displaying a
flashing amber light.

A   You would cross over
the first carriageway then
wait in the gap in the
central reservation. Be
careful, if you are towing
or if your vehicle is long,
that you do not cause other
road users to change
course or slow down.
B   You would wait until
there is a gap in the traffic
long enough for you safely
to clear the first
carriageway and emerge
into the second.

The speed limit applies to
all lanes. Use the first lane
to travel in and the second
for overtaking.

A   Dual carriageway ends
B   Road narrows on both
sides
C   Two-way traffic
straight ahead

A and C

Part 12

Driving an automatic car

Questions on pages 72 - 75

A1

Clutch

A2

1 Driving is easier
2 There is more time to concentrate on the road

A3

Park — Locks the transmission. This should be selected only when the vehicle is stationary.
Reverse — Enables the car to go backwards, as in a manual car.
Neutral — Has the same function as in a manual car. The engine is not in contact with the driving wheels.
Drive — Is used for driving forwards. It automatically selects the most appropriate gear.
3rd ⎤
2nd ⎟
1st ⎦ Have the same function as manual gears

A4

3

A5

1 Yes
2 No
3 Yes, if you needed extra control
4 You would probably use kickdown, but possibly in certain circumstances you would manually select a lower gear
5 Yes, maybe using 1st gear
6 No. Use the brakes

A6

1 The right foot
2 The right foot

A7

It stops you trying to control the brake and accelerator at the same time. It encourages early release of the accelerator and progressive braking.

A8

Drive, reverse, all forward gears.

A9

1 You should apply the handbrake every time you stop. Otherwise you have to keep your foot on the foot-brake.

A10

Park (P) or Neutral (N)

A11

1

Part 13

The driving test

Questions on pages 76 - 81

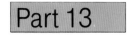

A1

1 False
2 True
3 False
4 False
5 True

A2

3

A3

False. If you did not hear clearly or did not understand what the examiner said, you should ask him or her to repeat the instruction. If you have any problem with your hearing, it is advisable to tell the examiner at the start of the test.

No. The standard of the test does not vary. The test result should be the same wherever it is taken.

1,4

2

The test will not proceed. You have failed not only the eyesight section, but the whole test. Remember, if you wear glasses or contact lenses, to wear them for the eyesight test and for the rest of the driving test.

provisional licence, signed

False. You can make some minor errors and still reach the required standard.

False. You will be asked to stop your car as if in an emergency and two of the other three manoeuvres.

Yes, but remember to do it up again when you have completed the exercise.

1 Give you a verbal explanation of the main reasons for failure
2 Write out a form for you to take away showing you your main errors

1 Drive unsupervised
2 Drive on a motorway
3 Drive without L-plates

No. You must have had at least three years' driving experience (and be over 21 years of age).

To the DVLA, Swansea

Yes. It is a good idea to keep a note of your driver number and the date you passed your test.

rules
high speed

2 The examiner will expect you to drive normally. You should abide by all speed limits and drive according to road and traffic conditions.

Yes. The examiner will be skilled in giving instructions and directions to deaf candidates.

Beyond the test
Questions on pages 82 - 83

No

1 Bad weather driving
2 Night-time driving
3 Motorway driving
4 Skid control...and more

2

A4

1, although people of any age can find it difficult to drive at night

A5

70

A6

There are certain serious driving offences which carry the penalty of disqualification. In order to regain a full licence, the disqualified driver has to apply for a provisional licence and take an extended test. If, because of certain illnesses, you have been unable to drive for 10 years, you will be required to take the test again in order to gain a full licence.

Motorway driving
Questions on pages 84 - 87

A7

1

A8

1 No
2 Yes
3 No
4 Yes
5 Yes
6 Yes
7 No

A9

1 Oil
2 Water
3 Fuel
4 Tyre pressures
These are some of the checks. You should take the advice given in the HMSO publication *Driving*.

A10

3 You should never attempt to retrieve anything from the carriageway.

A11

3

A12

B Amber
A Red
D Green
C White

A13

3

A14

Yes

A15

3

A16

1 False
2 False
3 False
4 True
5 False

A17

1, except when traffic is moving slowly in queues and the queue on the right is travelling more slowly

Safe night-time driving
Questions on pages 88 - 89

A18

2

A19

Switch on earlier, switch off later.

A20

1. It helps others to see you.

A21

If you are stationary, to avoid danger from a moving vehicle.

A22

A. Always park with the flow of traffic. You will show red reflectors to vehicles travelling in your direction.

1 Pedestrians ⎤ two
2 Cyclists   ⎬ of
3 Motor cyclists ⎦ these

In poor weather
conditions See
and be seen

dazzle
handbrake

**All-weather
driving**
Questions on pages
90 - 91

4

double

aquaplaning

2

1

very light

2

1 Slow down
2 stop
3 windscreen
wipers
4 demister, heated
rear windscreen

100 metres/yards

2

2

1 windows, audio
system.
Listen
2 early
3 brakes, alert
4 horn, warn

False, because
your tyres are not in
contact with
the road

brakes

1 gently
2 lower gear
3 drop, brakes

1

If possible, control
your speed before
reaching the hill.
Select a low gear
early.

Using your brakes

Avoid harsh
acceleration

1 The driver
2 The vehicle
3 The road
conditions

1 Slowing
2 Speeding
3 Turning
4 uphill, downhill

Part 15

Vehicle care
Questions on pages
96 - 97

1

Oil

3

Water, anti-freeze, air

1

dazzle

clean

uneven, bulges, cuts

2

Get them checked as
quickly as possible

Breakdowns,
accidents and
emergencies
Questions on pages
98 - 103

1   Neglect
2   routine checks
3   preventative
4   abuse

1   50m/yds
2   At least 150m/yds

Yes. Try to give as
much warning as
possible.

3

3

Under the drawing of
the handset is an arrow
which points to the
nearest telephone.

1   The emergency number
(painted on the box)
2   Vehicle details (make,
registration mark, colour)
3   Membership details of your
motoring organisation
4   Details of the fault

1   By displaying a Help
pennant
2   By using a mobile
telephone

A19
1   passing motorists
2   do not know
3   leave, longer

A20
1   False.   Do not move
injured people unless they are
in danger.
2   False.   Tell them the
facts, not what you think is
wrong.
3   False.   Do not give those
injured anything to eat or
drink. Keep them warm and
reassure them.
4   False.   Keep hazard lights
on to warn other drivers.
5   True.   Switch off engines.
Put out cigarettes.
6   True,   in the case of injury.

Stop

No

1   The other driver's name, address and contact number
2   The registration numbers of all the vehicles involved
3   The make of the other car
4   The other driver's insurance details
5   If the driver is not the owner, the owner's details

1   Pull up quickly
2   Get all passengers out
3   Call assistance

1   First aid
2   Fire extinguisher
3   Warning triangle

3

The motor car and the environment
Questions on pages 104 - 105

carbon dioxide, greenhouse

4

Yes

False. A catalytic convertor reduces the level of carbon monoxide, nitrogen oxide and hydrocarbons by up to 90 per cent. Carbon dioxide is still produced.

2

2

2

Nine measures are listed here:
1   Make sure your vehicle is in good condition and regularly serviced.
2   Make sure tyres are correctly inflated. Under-inflated tyres waste fuel.

3   Push the choke in as soon as possible when starting from cold.
4   Avoid harsh braking.
5   Buy a fuel-efficient vehicle.
6   Use the most appropriate gear.
7   Use your accelerator sensibly and avoid harsh acceleration.
8   Use unleaded fuel.
9   Dispose of waste oil, old batteries and used tyres sensibly.

Buying a used car
Questions on pages 106 - 107

dealer, auction, privately

Why is it being sold?

1   True
2   False
3   True
4   True

1   What is covered
2   The length of the agreement

taxed, MOT, insurance

A40

Four items to check are listed here:
1 Mileage
2 Has it been involved in any accidents?
3 Number of owners
4 Is there any hire purchase or finance agreement outstanding?

A41

True. The AA offer a national inspection scheme.

Part 16

Towing a caravan or trailer

Questions on pages 108 - 109

A1

1

A2

Exterior towing mirrors, to give you a good view

A3

2

A4

stabiliser

A5

3

A6

A   2
B   2

A7

Seven checks are listed here:
1 Is the caravan or trailer loaded correctly?
2 Is it correctly hitched up to your vehicle?
3 Are the lights and indicators working properly?
4 Is the braking system working correctly?
5 Is the jockey wheel assembly fully retracted and in the correct position?
6 Are tyre pressures correct?
7 Are all windows, doors and roof lights closed?

A8

jockey wheel, corner steadies

Driving on the Continent

Questions on page 110 - 111

A9

vehicle, documents

A10

1 route
2 motoring regulations

A11

Here are five routine checks:
1 Tyres, including spare. Always carry a spare tyre.
2 Tool kit and jack.
3 Lamps and brake lights.
4 Fit deflectors to your headlampsto prevent dazzle to other drivers approaching on the left.
5 Check you have an extra exterior mirror on the left.

A12

driving licence

A13

International Driving Permit

A14

Some non-EC countries

A15

2

A16

Five items are listed here:
1 Spare lamps and bulbs
2 Warning triangle
3 First aid kit
4 Fire extinguisher
5 Emergency windscreen